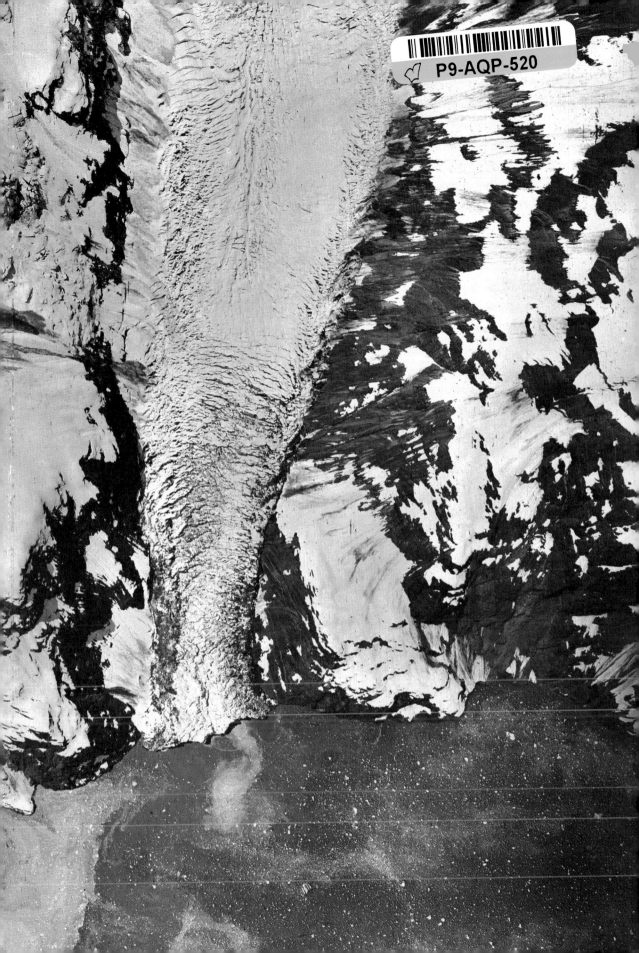

THE EARTH
IN ACTION

Cooperating Publishers

Collins—Great Britain
Flammarion—France
McGraw-Hill—United States
Rizzoli—Italy
Schreiber—Germany

International Committee of Consultants

Jean-François Poupinel — France
Ancien Élève École Polytechnique

Klaus Doderer — Germany
Professor, Frankfurt

Margaret Meek — Great Britain
Lecturer in Education at Goldsmiths' College in the University of London

Fausto Maria Bongioanni — Italy
Professor of Education at the University of Genoa

Mary V. Gaver — United States of America
Professor, Graduate School of Library Science, Rutgers University

INTERNATIONAL LIBRARY

MARGARET O. HYDE

THE EARTH
IN ACTION

McGRAW-HILL BOOK COMPANY

New York · St. Louis · San Francisco

For Bill, Tricia and Linda Parker

CONTENTS

CHAPTER I

THE VIEW
FROM SPACE

Suppose visitors came from another planet searching for life on the planet earth. Their mission, Destination Earth, is a purely scientific one. The earth is not an outstanding part of the universe because of its size or position, even though it is so necessary to the people who live on it. In fact, the earth is a very, very insignificant speck in the geography of the universe. It is but a small part of the solar system centered on the sun that is only an average-sized star and is one of only average brilliance despite its brightness in the earth's sky.

The solar system itself is not especially impressive, in spite of the fact that it is about ten billion miles in diameter. It belongs to the Milky Way Galaxy, a vast complex of stars which probably number as many as a hundred billion stars. Even the Milky Way is of no great importance when compared with the total number of galaxies in the universe. There are billions of galaxies, each with billions of stars, and many of the stars may have systems that include planets. Some astronomers estimate that the universe must teem with more than one hundred trillion civilizations.

In the constellation Andromeda there is a great galaxy called M 31,

which is similar to the Milky Way Galaxy in appearance. Both galaxies have spiral arms that swirl out from the brightly star-packed center. Of course, in each one distances are so vast that the stars are actually billions of miles apart, but from a distance they appear to be close together. Suppose dwellers on a planet in the M 31 galaxy leave on a mission to search for a planet in the Milky Way Galaxy, that might be a twin to one in M 31, somewhat the way the two galaxies are thought of as twins.

Their journey begins about 2.2 million light years away. Each light year is the distance it takes light to travel in one year, and since light travels at a speed of 186,000 miles per second, a light year is about six trillion miles. No one can begin to comprehend such a long journey.

The Earth in Motion

Perhaps the explorers are traveling in some state that resembles the way animals hibernate in winter. Now they are nearing the planet earth, and they have been revived. They see earth revolving around the sun in an elliptical path, a journey of 600 million miles. The path is not a circle because the distance of the earth from the sun varies by

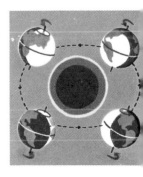

The seasons change according to the tilt of the earth

more than three million miles during the course of a year. Strange as it may seem, the varying distance from the sun is not the reason for the change in the earth's seasons. In fact, in the Northern Hemisphere the earth s nearer the sun in the wintertime. Almost everyone knows that the tilt of the earth's axis as it travels around the sun causes the sun's rays to strike at various angles. Where the rays hit at a higher angle to the earth's surface it is warmer. Whether or not space visitors journeying toward the earth would discover this seasonal change before nearing the earth, no one knows.

The most obvious motion to an observer in a space ship is the turning of the earth on its axis, which causes day and night as an area turns into the sunlight and then away from it.

An observer in space would certainly notice the moon as it travels in its path around the earth during a twenty-eight-day period. As the moon circles the earth, its pull causes the center of the earth to trace an erratic curve in its path around the sun. This slight wobble in the earth's orbit is not the only imperfection in its apparently broad and even sweep.

The earth wobbles a bit on its axis as it rotates, for the weight of the tides causes a slight imbalance in the earth's spin. Since this wobble takes place slowly, a voyager from outer space would not notice it, but astronomers on earth compare it to the wobbling of a top. Of course the wobbling is very slow and the "top" is very large.

During the course of about 26,000 years, another movement takes place. Scientists call it the precession of the equinoxes. The North Star changes from Vega to Polaris because the tilt of the earth's axis changes very slightly. Today it is moving in the direction of Polaris. In 2100 A.D. the axis will begin to move in a direction opposite the present one, and by 14,000 A.D. the North Star will be Vega rather than Polaris, as it is at present.

There are other slight motions of the earth as it moves through the space traveler's sky, but he will not notice them. He will, however, be calculating the motion of the entire solar system. The sun is moving at a speed of twelve miles per second in the general direction of the constellation Hercules. Along with it go the earth and the other planets of the solar system. The whole solar system also travels around the hub of the Milky Way Galaxy in a sweep that takes 250 million years to complete even though it is traveling at a speed of 480,000 miles per hour.

Even the Milky Way is moving through space. Scientists know this because of its relationships in space to other galaxies. No one knows exactly where it is heading, but its direction is of no great importance to man on earth or even to a space traveler who might be on his way to visit earth from another planet of another solar system.

The many movements of the earth are complex. No one fully comprehends them, even though scientists can measure many exact speeds and distances. Astronomers can even measure the distance of an object whose light began its journey to earth many billions of years ago, and light travels six million million

The Milky Way has many stars. The sun and earth are located near one edge of the Milky Way

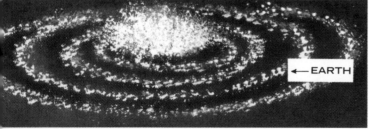

←EARTH

miles per year. But any traveler from space who came to visit the earth would have an awareness of the vastness of the universe and the comparative smallness of the planet he had chosen to visit.

From thirty-five million miles away, through the space ship's telescope, the earth might appear as a bluish disk with no evidence of life. Although clouds cover some of the earth's large features, the oceans and land areas could be distinguished. From nearer by, the earth would make a more interesting picture. The moon circling it would be grey in color, the oceans would be blue-green, and the land masses would be a pale red-brown with patches of green where foliage is thickest. From four hundred miles away, the coastlines, rivers, and some vegetation could be seen, but there would still be no sign of animal life. If a space visitor remained in orbit high above the earth for a long period of time, he could watch the color changes on the land masses as the seasons produced changes in vegetation and snow cover.

To an earth dweller, views of the earth from space are spectacularly beautiful. Looking up into the sky,

The earth revolves on its axis

A one-hundred-foot spherical satellite is inspected by scientists before it is sent aloft

he has never appreciated the vastness of the clouds. But pictures taken by astronauts preparing for moon trips and pictures taken by satellites have begun to provide earthmen with views from unprecedented vantage points. Rockets, satellites, and space probes are helping men to paint a new picture of the earth on which they live.

A visitor from outer space who comes to examine the planet earth may or may not find many things exciting to him. But man, who has lived here for close to a million years, is beginning to piece together a dramatic story.

Some scientists believe that the most important information that comes from satellites will be about the earth itself. Certainly, the view from space is revolutionizing man's view of the earth and the atmosphere that clings around it.

Space Age View of the Earth

From the beginning of the space age, when the grapefruit-sized Vanguard began orbiting, ideas have been changing. Perhaps from the time that man realized that the earth was not flat he thought of it as a perfect sphere. Then he realized, from careful measurements, that it was slightly flattened at the poles. From the little satellite Vanguard's gravitational data, scientists observed that the earth is very slightly humped at the North Pole though in general flatter than other areas, and very slightly bulged in the Southern Hemisphere in somewhat the way a pear is shaped. These irregularities are extremely

The Vanguard satellite readied for flight

The doughnut-shaped Van Allen belt surrounds the earth

small compared with the size of the earth, but they do exist, and it took a view from space to make man aware of them.

In 1965 the old round-ball concept of the earth changed even more as the result of data from satellites. Four large patches of the earth appear to be abnormally elevated and four unusually depressed. These vast areas are much larger than mountains or valleys. One elevation stretches from a region south of the tip of Africa halfway to Australia, and one of the "bowls," or depressed areas, runs along the vicinity of the North American West Coast from the Aleutians to California. Such discoveries about the earth may or may not be noticed by a visitor from another planet, but they are important to men on earth

in improving intercontinental navigation and in better understanding the earth's structure.

Another amazing discovery about the earth was made early in the space age, when data from Explorer satellites led to the recognition of the Van Allen belt, which surrounds the earth at a height of 40,000 miles or more. This belt consists of invisibly small particles of matter that produce radiation. This amazing radiation belt has caused much excitement among scientists.

Satellites have confirmed the existence of a tremendous solar wind, which blows steadily from the sun in all directions at tremendous speeds. The wind is not the same kind as wind near the earth, which consists of tremendous numbers of molecules of the gases of the earth's

Solar winds constantly bombard the earth

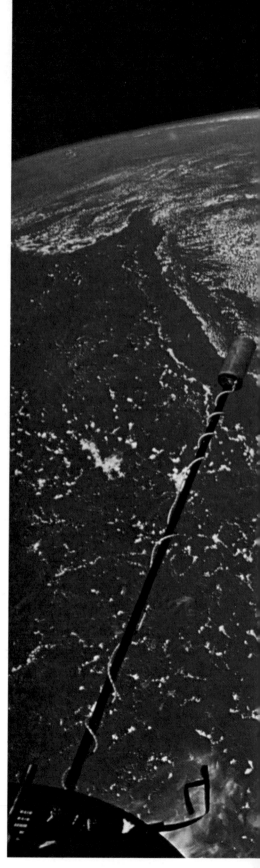

atmosphere. The solar wind consists of charged particles from the sun; it is a very thin gas that boils off from the sun at speeds of up to two million miles an hour. There are particles of hydrogen, helium, and other electrically charged particles in the solar wind, but the density of the wind is very thin indeed by the time it reaches the earth.

An envelope of magnetized gases surrounds the earth and protects it from much of the radiation of the solar wind. At one time this magnetic envelope was thought to be circular, so it was called the magnetosphere. Shortly before 1960, scientists proposed that the solar wind probably pushed some of the magnetosphere in such a way that the earth possessed a magnetic tail. No one knew how far such a tail stretched out, but it was believed to be very long.

The subcontinent of India lies over one hundred miles below a Gemini spacecraft

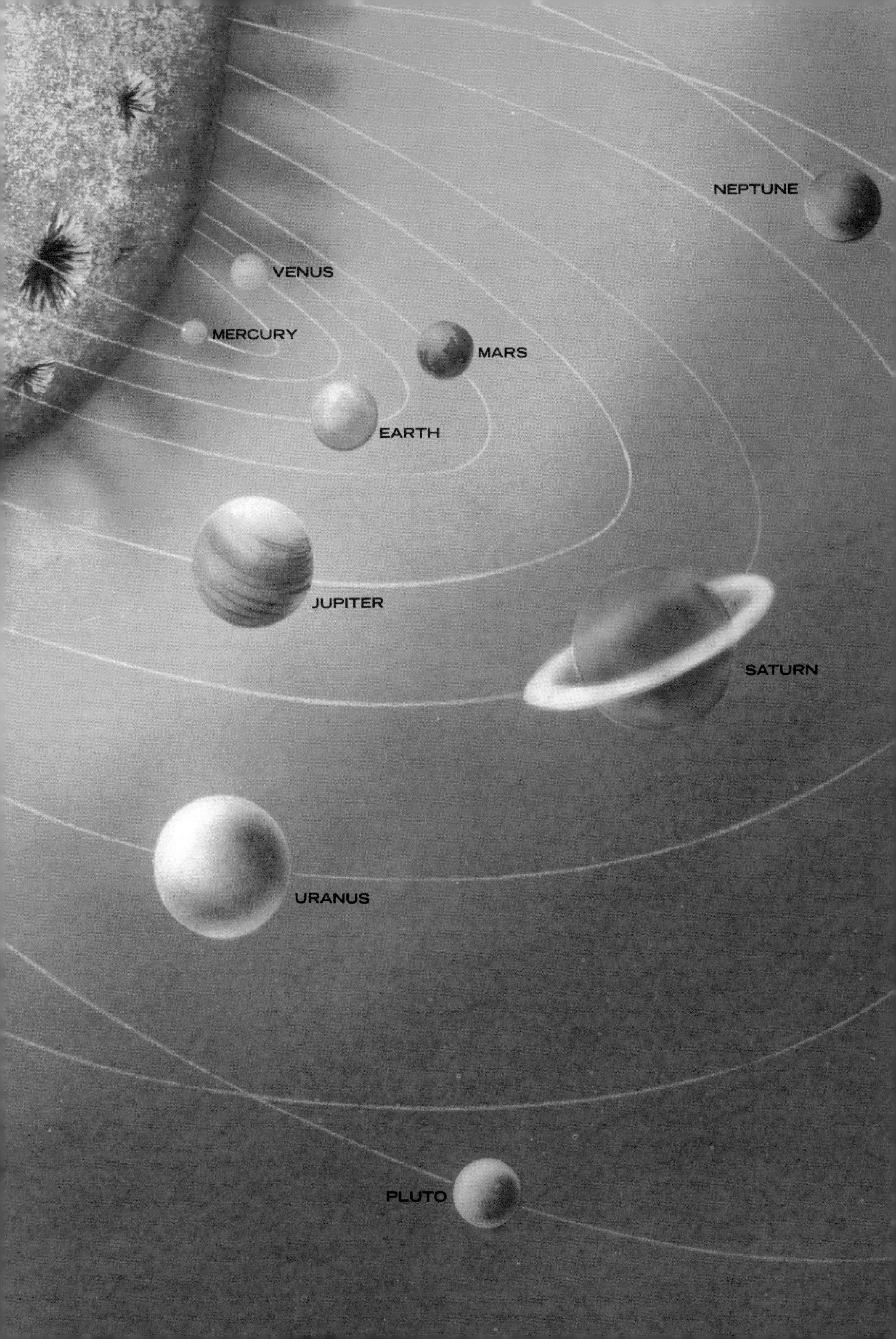
NEPTUNE
VENUS
MERCURY
MARS
EARTH
JUPITER
SATURN
URANUS
PLUTO

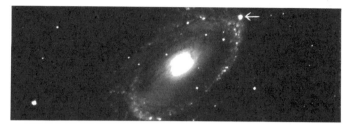

The marker in the lower picture points to a nova, or new star

In 1966, Pioneer 7 was launched to search for the tail as far out as it possibly could and thus measure it. At a distance of about 3.2 million miles from the earth, Pioneer 7's instruments indicated that it had flown from the flow of solar particles, or solar wind, into a protective area, which was the earth's magnetic tail. It then reemerged into the solar wind, which traveled at a speed of one to two million miles per hour, repenetrated the magnetic tail, and reentered the solar wind in such a pattern that scientists were led to believe that the tail was flapping back and forth. Scientists still have much to learn about the vast solar winds that buffet areas around the earth and the effects such winds have on the earth's weather. Such probes into space have brought tantalizing hints of exciting discoveries that probably lie ahead.

Scientists have been excited for a number of years by the photographs of the earth from space, which they piece together to show the entire world in one picture. Some weather satellites scan the earth, showing landmarks and cloud areas by making rapid-fire heat readings and radioing them back to earth. Newer types of color photographs show the entire surface of the earth from pole to pole; they are taken from satellites that travel about 20,000 miles above the earth's surface.

Tremendous numbers of photographs of global weather patterns are helping meteorologists around the world to improve their forecasts. Some lenses in the cameras of satellites show amazingly detailed photographs from high in the sky.

Teams of scientists are working together with views of the earth from space. For example, they are making better maps. They measure the position of a satellite in relation to its star background from a number of observation posts at different places on the earth. They determine the angles between adjacent stations. Such world-wide networks are improving map making to the extent that a measurement will be no more than one foot in variation for every 500,000 feet of linear distance. Using satellites, scientists have already been able to determine the degree of the polar flattening of the earth about ten times more precisely than formerly.

Project Eros, a system of Earth Resources Observation Satellites, is a particularly interesting use of space to study the earth, for it is aimed at gathering facts about the earth's natural resources from satellites that carry sophisticated remote-sensing instruments. Water and mineral supply information and a vast amount of other information can be obtained for the entire globe and it can be put to work to help men cope with problems brought about by population and industrial growth.

Certainly, the view of earth from space is just beginning to help men learn about the world in which they live. It is exciting and challenging to think of what an important part the view from space can play in the future.

CHAPTER II

THE BIRTH
AND DEATH
OF THE EARTH

One of the most fascinating riddles is the one of how the earth began. Scientists believe that our sun is a second-generation star made of matter that was left over when another star exploded. The earth and man would also be made from second-generation atoms left over from a cosmic explosion billions of years ago.

No one has exact answers to questions about the creation of the earth, but scientists are continually searching for better answers to the riddle. Since no one witnessed the earth's creation, it is not surprising that many different stories have been handed down through the ages.

The first recorded attempt to explain the birth of the earth was made by the Sumerians, a people who lived between the Tigris and Euphrates Rivers about 3000 B.C. These people believed in a god, Enil, who was their god of air. Enil wrenched the heaven and earth from a mountain where his parents dwelled. His father was god of heaven and his mother was goddess of the earth. Their mountain was believed to have arisen from an eternal sea.

The earth the Sumerians pictured was a flat circle of land with a rounded vault above it. The sun, moon, and various stars were thought to be swirling in the air between heaven and earth.

The ancient Egyptians pictured the earth as a reclining god, Keb, covered by vegetation. A god of the atmosphere held the goddess of heaven in a gracefully curved position above the earth.

Perhaps it might seem that one guess is as good as another when it comes to explaining the creation of the earth, but modern scientists have based their theories on laws that they believe operate throughout the universe.

Modern Theories of How the Earth Began

One theory that was popular with scientists not long ago is known as the collision theory. We know that stars are separated by trillions of miles and that the chances of a meeting or a near collision of two stars is very unlikely. But suppose that long ago a star passed close to our star, the sun. Even from a distance of a few million miles, it would have exerted a tremendous pull on the sun, and great bulges would have developed in the gases of the sun.

Imagine two gaseous jets shooting out from the sun as the star approached it. Scientists who sug-

An aerial view of Geikie Glacier, Alaska. Showing: icebergs, crevasses, and moraines

gested this theory thought of the jets as tremendous bulges. One jet—the one moving toward the star—could have become the planet Neptune, and the one on the opposite side could have become the planet Mars. Then a second pair of jets composed of sun material might have been pulled away by the star that passed near the sun. They might have produced a second pair of planets, Uranus and the earth. In similar manner, the beginnings of the planets Saturn, Venus, Jupiter, and Mercury might have come from successive jets of sun material. When the gases cooled, some of the material condensed into liquid and then into solid masses. Count-

less particles of sun material was thought to have added to the size of the planets as they spun around the sun. Since these bits of matter were called planetisimals, this theory of the birth of the planets has been called the planetisimal hypothesis as well as the collision theory.

Many mysteries were left unexplained by the planetisimal hypothesis, as they were by most other theories. But today most scientists seem to agree on a theory that explains the birth of the sun as well as the birth of the earth and other planets. This theory comes closer to satisfying both the laws of astronomy and the words of the Bible than any of the others.

Cosmic Dust Could Have Formed the Earth

Cosmic dust, fine particles of matter spread thinly through space, drifts like tremendous puffs of smoke through vast areas of the universe. Try to imagine such a cloud that is five trillion miles in diameter. If you are having a difficult time, you are not alone, for it is really impossible to do. One cannot imagine a cloud that is even a billion or a million miles in diameter. But such clouds do exist. In such vast clouds, one tiny frozen particle of matter is present in every five cubic miles of nothing. From such a cloud of dust that was floating through space driven by the force of distant starlight, the earth may have been born.

In the case of the cloud that spawned the earth and its planets, the force of light pushed particles in the cosmic cloud closer together. This made the cloud smaller, and the streams of dust moving through it had more chance of colliding. Some particles remained far apart, some just missed each other, and some hit each other. Large quantities of matter were built of those particles that collided, and they began to swirl toward the center of the cloud.

Just as everything on the earth is drawn toward the center by the force of gravity, so particles of dust were drawn toward the center of the cloud. This cosmic mass grew as it spiraled inward, somewhat the way a snowball grows by gathering snow as it rolls down a hill, but at a slower rate. This was the beginning of the sun.

At some point, the formless cloud became a flattened revolving sphere with a cool, large concentration of matter in the center and much smaller masses of cosmic dust spinning around it in a series of rings. The central mass, the protosun, probably consisted of as much as 90 percent of the original matter in the cosmic cloud, leaving 10 percent for the protoplanets, which became the planets. The stars in the distant

Cosmic dust may have collected into stars and planets, resulting in the formation of groups such as the solar system

sky provided little light in the area where the sun was being born, but there was enough light to play a part in the following action.

As the ball at the center was compressed by the pressure of light from neighboring stars, there was an increase in the pull of gravity toward the center of it. This in turn caused further compression. Increased pressure caused the temperature to rise inside the protosun to such a great degree that atoms of hydrogen gas were changed into helium gas by a process known as thermonuclear reaction, or fusion. Fusion is accompanied by the release of a huge amount of energy through a process similar to that in

From the creation of the sun, perhaps as long ago as five or more billion years, until the present time, heat from fusion in the sun has warmed the earth. It will continue to do so until most of the sun's hydrogen is used. In the meantime, every day the earth basks in solar energy equivalent to the amount of energy that would be produced by burning 500,000 tons of coal.

The Earth in the Beginning

Such was not the case when the earth was very young. Protoearth was a cool earth, getting hotter as it grew. No one knows how the

In the process of fission, atoms break apart; in fusion, they combine. Each process releases energy

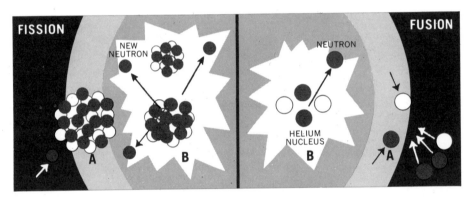

an exploding hydrogen bomb. Of course, the sun is many, many times more powerful.

The core of the sun is a nuclear reactor in which hydrogen nuclei collide with such violence that they fuse. Fusion is the opposite of fission, or splitting of atomic nuclei, the process by which today's nuclear reactors at atomic power plants provide the energy for the production of electricity. In the fusion process, the nuclei of atoms combine. Matter changes to energy and tremendous amounts of heat are produced. The temperature at the center of the sun is estimated to be about twenty-five million degrees Fahrenheit.

earth became solid, but as it grew larger from bits of matter that fell on it, its gravitational attraction grew stronger. Small bodies of cosmic dust hit harder and faster and released larger amounts of energy with their impact. This may have helped to heat the earth, but there were other factors involved, too. As the earth grew, it must have become very hot from the friction between it and the particles of the solar cloud through which it passed.

Many astronomers believe that the core of the earth was less than 2,000 degrees Fahrenheit during its first 500 million years. That is cool compared with what it probably is now, about 6,700 degrees Fahrenheit.

The earth grew from the addition of clusters of bodies such as meteorites, which still hit it today. The early ones were probably composed of much the same material as the recent ones, which are mostly metallic iron and silicate rock mixed together. You probably are well acquainted with the silicon dioxide of the coasts, common sand. The iron in the earth is present today mostly deep inside the earth. Here is the reason.

In addition to silicates and iron, other chemicals helped form the young earth, and some of them were radioactive. Such elements decay and give off heat as they do so. For millions of years the energy given off by radioactive elements heated the earth until some of the materials melted. Because of its lower melt-

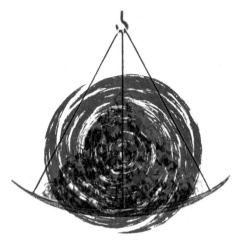

The energy received in one day from the heat of the sun is equal to that produced by 500,000 tons of coal

ing point the iron became liquid first, and since it was heavier than most elements, it sank toward the center of the earth. As a result, silicates deep inside the earth floated

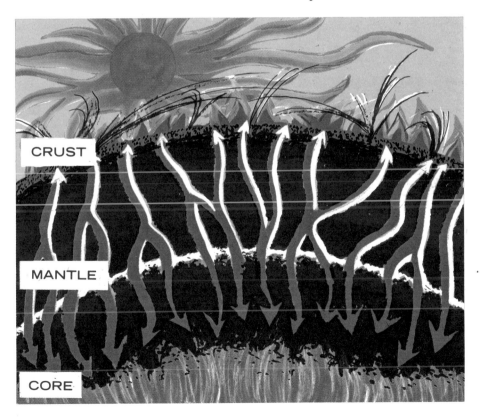

CRUST

MANTLE

CORE

Early volcanoes formed within the hot earth and lava flowed toward the surface

21

upward to become part of the crust. There was a moving of material on a gigantic scale.

Can you imagine what the motion described above did to the surface of the earth? The surface probably bubbled furiously for a long period of time, while the heavy material was sinking toward the core and the lighter material rising to the top. Great bursts of carbon dioxide and water vapor spewed forth from the interior. Smoke and flame were fierce and ever present. Molten rock poured from the deep in huge fountains. This violent action may have continued for hundreds, thousands, or even millions of years.

The original gases that formed the earth, the gases of the cosmic cloud, were almost entirely lost in space for they were mainly hydrogen and helium. Such light gases drifted off, while small amounts of methane and ammonia gases may have combined chemically with the rock.

The Earth's Atmosphere

Certainly the gases around the young earth were very different from those in today's atmosphere. The 90 percent hydrogen and 9 percent helium of the original atmosphere is the same material of which most of the starry universe is made. About one percent of the primeval atmosphere was made of elements that are common on the earth at present. There is very little free hydrogen (hydrogen that is not combined chemically with another element) and relatively little helium present in the earth now. Strangely enough, it has been estimated that the water that existed as a gas at the time of the earth's birth was so scarce that it would have brought the depth of the oceans only to a small fraction of an inch. The water that covers so much of the earth at present came from chemical compounds in the rock that were eventually forced out by heat.

Both the oceans and the atmosphere in which life developed were derived largely from the interior of the earth. It is possible that the oceans have grown in volume during millions of years of time and are still slowly continuing to grow.

No one knows how rapidly the oceans and the atmosphere were formed, but it seems likely that after most of the iron reached the center, the earth became more quiet. It began to cool, and a thin, fairly calm crust formed, the crust on which we live. Some scientists believe that the cooling process is still taking place today. Certainly,

Radiation ocean dumps pollute sea water

22

The scientist Sir Ernest Rutherford first convinced other scientists that the earth was at least seven hundred million years old

their ideas about the age of the earth.

The Age of the Earth

When did the earth form? From time to time in the past men have offered exact dates. Today's scientists measure the age of the earth in billions of years. They do not guess, for they have ways of measuring that are based on scientific laws. Even so, estimates change.

The new science of dating uses a number of methods. Long ago scientists were able to establish major periods in the history of the earth by reading records of fossils in rocks. Lesser divisions were measured too, but more exact dating did not come until comparatively recently. The more exact methods led scientists to believe that the earth is far older than it was first supposed.

There is a story told about Ernest Rutherford, a famous scientist who

volcanoes continue to erupt.

No one knows whether the above ideas are true, but they are the best that scientists can find to explain how the earth began. Their ideas about it are still changing, as are

Fossil fish such as these in sedimentary rocks gave man an idea of ancient life

spent some time working at McGill University in Montreal, Canada. One day when he was walking across the McGill campus, he asked a geologist how old he thought the earth was. The geologist answered that most scientists felt it must be about a hundred million years old. True, indeed; the earth was at least that old, but most people believed it was no older than that. Rutherford tossed a piece of pitchblende, a black mineral containing uranium and some other radioactive materials, in his hand. Then he announced that he knew that the pitchblende was *seven* hundred million years old. Since the pitchblende was dug from the earth, it could hardly be older than the earth.

Rutherford had good reason to believe that the earth was many times older than the scientists of his day had estimated, for he knew how to date the age of rocks by calculating the age of the uranium and lead in the pitchblende.

Uranium decays into lead at a fixed rate known to scientists. Half of any given quantity of uranium decays and becomes a special kind of lead, called radiogenic lead, at the end of four and a half billion years. This is called the half life of uranium. Half of the remaining uranium will decay in exactly the same period of time, and so on, and so on.

Suppose you had a piece of pitchblende that was unweathered and unaltered in any way from the natural state in which it was found in the earth. The radiogenic lead in the uranium ore is a product of decay of uranium. By measuring the ratio of the radiogenic lead to the uranium, the age of the uranium could be determined. There are some complications to this kind of dating that need not be discussed

here, but it is true that Rutherford's way of finding the age of a piece of ore was fairly accurate. This method is known as uranium dating.

Since the introduction of uranium dating, other methods have been developed that also enable scientists to pry the age from a piece of silent rock. Some of these different ways are more efficient than the uranium-lead method. One popular method of dating the past is by measuring a form of carbon known as carbon-14 in objects that were once alive. This method is very precise, but it does not help with objects more than 50,000 years old.

Not long ago, the age of the earth was set at four and a half billion years, give or take 200 million years. This was far older than previous estimates. In 1967, Dr. V. I. Baranov of the U.S.S.R. Academy of Sciences reported that he believed the earth may be at least six billion years old. Measurements are being made only from the materials in the earth's crust, and such matter may not have mixed with chemicals deep within the earth that may be older than the crust. Other scientists question

Petrified wood looks like wood, but is actually solid rock

A piece of meteorite exhibits its inner structure

Pitchblende is a rock containing radioactive minerals

A fossil shell lies embedded in shale; scientists studying such fossils have been able to date certain rocks

Sections of meteorites can be very beautiful

whether man has ever found a rock that could qualify as part of the original crust of the earth.

Certainly two things are true. No one knows exactly when and how the earth was created, and it is very old. It is old compared with the life span of living things or even compared with how long life on earth has existed. But compared with its own expected life span, the earth is a young earth. It is not nearing its end.

The Death of the Earth

From time to time people have predicted exact dates for the end of the earth. Although many nonscientists have stated times as exact as the hour and even the minute, scientists agree that it will end but that no one knows just when.

The earth depends on the sun, and the sun gets its energy by using the hydrogen of which it is made. When will this fusion powerhouse run out of fuel? Astronomers estimate that the sun will continue to produce energy by fusion for about three to five billion more years. When the fuel supply dwindles to a certain level, when the amount of hydrogen left in the sun is no longer enough to continue the same kind of nuclear reactions, strange things will happen. Different kinds of reactions will begin in the core that will cause the already tremendous sun to swell larger and larger until it may be twenty or more times the size it is today. It will be so large that it will extend about one quarter of the way to the planet Mercury, or perhaps far beyond it.

As the sun grows old, the wild series of explosions that will cause its expansions will send out such heat to the earth that the side facing the sun will be ablaze in a short time. As the earth turns its dark side toward the sun, it too will be heated so that the mountains will melt and incandescent rocks will roll into the valleys.

That is one theory scientists have about the death of the earth. Another belief is that the sun may explode all at once and become what is known as a supernova. If such is the case, the earth would turn to gas in a matter of minutes. That seems less likely than the series of explosions; but whatever the case may be, you need not be concerned about it happening in your lifetime. And whether there is one or many explosions, the earth seems destined to end in a fiery state.

The dying sun, having used its energy, will shrink to a small fraction of its original size. By then the earth will be a featureless and blackened cinder. It will probably continue to circle around the dying sun, but no one will be there to watch for the dawn. Eventually, some greater catastrophe may return the earth to cosmic dust much the same as that from which it developed.

When the sun dies it will at first become larger, but as it loses heat it will become smaller

CHAPTER III

THE ROCKY

CRUST

Suppose the earth were stripped of its water and one could see just the bare, rocky surface, as one sees the surface of the moon. How would a dry earth look from an orbiting space ship? Ocean basins and continents would be the most obvious features, with the continents rising as vast plateaus about three miles above the ocean floors. The majestic mountains of the continents and the submarine mountains and canyons might look like ruffles or decorations on a cake compared with the height of the continents above the ocean basins themselves.

If one compares the whole rocky crust to the diameter of the earth, the crust seems very insignificant, for it is only about three to thirty miles thick compared with the distance to the center of the earth, which is about 4,000 miles. But the crust is the part you see, no matter where you look. The crust is the part you find, no matter how deeply you dig, even if the rock is belched from the mouths of volcanoes as far as thirty miles below the surface.

Rockhounds—those who collect rocks as a hobby—collect bits and pieces of the earth's crust. Builders quarry stones from it, and gem hunters dig for jewels deep inside.

And the cores men dig from deep beneath the ocean floor are part of the crust.

The continents of the earth have stood high above the ocean basins for several thousand million years, although vast areas of continents have had sea water on them at different times in the history of the changing earth. A simple model of the rocky crust would consist of a layer of basalt about three miles thick lying on the next deeper layer of the earth, the mantle. Basalt is a heavy black rock that is present throughout the ocean floor and under the continents, and it is much heavier than the giant blocks of rock, mostly granite, that form the continents.

Picture icebergs floating in the polar seas, with much of their ice submerged. Somewhat the same situation exists with the continents. Scientists believe that the mantle on which the crust lies is yielding. The continental blocks are lighter than the basalt, but they are so heavy that they press on it and push it down about fourteen miles into the mantle, much as an iceberg pushes down on the water in which it floats. The continents we know are part of great blocks of rock that continue down far below the surface of the land, for they average twenty

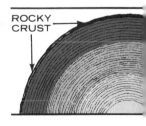

The rocky crust of the earth is very thin

GRENADE

The echo of sound waves traveling under water shows scientists the depth of the ocean

miles in thickness. The basalt averages only three miles above the ocean basins.

Dr. Carl O. Dunbar, a famous American geologist, has compared man to a penguin riding on an iceberg, for man rides on floating continents whose major parts are submerged.

Although the rocky crust of the earth seems so solid that people sometimes use the expression "solid as a rock," there has been, and continues to be, much activity there. Actually, scientists are not able to point to a single place that they know to be part of the primeval crust of the earth, although a new technique for charting the ocean floor beneath its blanket of sediment has discovered what may be a small section of the original crust. In a method developed by Dr. Maurice Ewing, director of Lamont Geological Observatory of Columbia University, and his colleagues, grenades are tossed overboard at regular two-minute intervals, and the sound of the explosions produces echoes not only from the sea-bottom but also

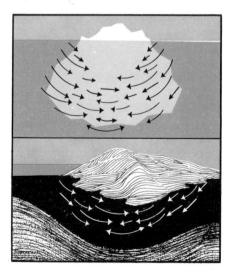

Solid granite floats in the rocky crust the way icebergs float in water

from the layers as much as three miles below the muck. These layers will indicate the possible location of the original crust.

Soil and Rocks

The scientists who probe deeply in the earth's crust with tools and the ones who study the earth just beneath your feet all agree that man has much to learn about the earth.

Have you ever looked at the soil beneath your feet and thought of it as a scientific laboratory? Soil does not sound like a very exciting subject, even though people are beginning to talk of it as a priceless heritage that must be guarded for men yet unborn. Aside from its value in agriculture, soil is a precious laboratory of chemicals that came from the rock that forms the earth's crust. Actually, soil is part of the earth's crust that has been broken into tiny little pieces by a process that has been going on for billions of years. Decaying plants add to it, and its whole chemistry is so complex that some scientists devote their careers to its study.

Agriculturalists can tell much about the soil, layer beneath layer. Perhaps you have dug in the soil and have noticed that the particles become coarser with depth until the parent bedrock is reached. At some places you might dig just a few inches, but in others there might be hundreds of feet of soil before rock is reached.

Few people make a hobby of soils; but rock collectors, or rockhounds, are numerous. From the interesting collections of very young children to those with rare specimens of great value, much can be learned and enjoyed.

One exciting approach to rock collecting is that of Dr. Lorence G.

Collins, who studies rocks from the artistic point of view. With a special kind of microscope, he photographs wafer-thin sections of rocks in colors that appear far more beautiful than the rocks themselves. Some rock crystals are magnified one hundred times after being sliced with a diamond saw so that they are just 1/1000th of an inch

If an ocean were dry, its bottom would look as rugged as this

This slice of granite, magnified forty times, has a beautiful mineral structure

thick. Dr. Collins compares some of the beautiful effects produced by nature to those produced by modern art, for the rocks produce striking patterns and colors.

Actually, geologists use the above type of specimen for more than the beautiful effects they create. By studying samples of crystals of various minerals, they learn their composition and how to change them and find clues to the presence of petroleum and metallic ores. Even moon rocks will be studied through a microscope that is made especially for the study of rocks.

Many rock collectors just try to see how many different kinds of rocks they can collect and identify. Some specialize in mineralogy, the study of minerals (chemical compounds that occur naturally in the earth from nonliving things). Others specialize in petrology, the study of rocks made of combinations of minerals; still others study paleontology, or fossilized specimens that were once alive. Fossils give exciting clues to the history of the earth.

Rock Collecting

Suppose you want to collect rocks, just any rocks that you think are attractive. How could you begin to label them? Since there

are more than a thousand kinds of minerals, it would be difficult to estimate the number of different possible combinations that form rocks. But there are three main kinds of rock, based on how they were formed. One kind of rock is sedimentary. Such rocks consist of layers of hardened sand, shells, rock fragments, and mud that were laid down millions of years ago, layer upon layer. Sandstone, which is sand cemented under pressure; limestone, which includes a variety of rocks containing calcium; shale, which is rock composed mainly of clay or mud; and conglomerate, which is coarsely fragmented rock, are common examples of sedimentary rocks. They cover about three quarters of the earth's surface.

Deep within the crust of the earth, there is molten material that sometimes reaches toward the surface through cracks or weakened places. Such material, known as magma, forms igneous rocks when it cools and solidifies at any part of the crust. Basalt and felsite are examples of igneous rocks.

The third kind of rock is metamorphic, or changed rock. When rocks are changed from their original variety by heat, pressure, or chemical action, a new kind of crystalline material, or a new mineral in the rock, or a change in the rock's texture may be present. Marble was once limestone, and slate, a fine-grained rock that splits into thin sheets, was once shale.

Classification of rocks is not an easy task. Even geologists do not always agree. For example, some believe that most granite is metamorphic rather than igneous in origin.

If you are interested in collecting rocks, there may be books in your local library or services connected with a local museum that will help

When viewed under fluorescent light, the colors of some minerals change

you identify your specimens, tell you where to look for rocks, suggest ways of arranging them, and provide other helpful information. Some states in the United States publish maps to help rockhounds locate interesting specimens. In Europe various government agencies help amateurs who are interested in rocks.

One kind of rock collecting that is gaining in popularity is gem hunting. Perhaps there is a lapidary club, or gem study group, in your school or neighborhood.

Experts make costly jewels from rough gem stones

In some areas, owners of places where semiprecious stones can be found help tourists on gem hunts. In the Alps, guides take mountain-climbing tourists to areas where they may find garnets embedded in the rocks, quartz crystals, or other interesting specimens. In Franklin, North Carolina, tourists are permitted to explore some mines on a pay-to-dig and finders-keepers basis. Chances of finding a valuable gem are slim, but the fee is only a few dollars for a day's digging and the tools with which to do it. There are other areas where tourists may pan for gold or search for uranium with a Geiger counter.

Since many gems look like ordinary stones when found in their natural location, amateur gem collectors need to know something

Mountain climbers often search for gem stones

34

about geology and rock formations.

Mining Precious Gems

At one time, treasures were more common in the earth's crust than they are now. Today the most obvious. ones have been found. Men must dig deeply in mines for many of the valuable ones. Gold miners in Africa have blasted through rock to a depth of over two miles. The South African Kimberly diamond mines are world-famous, as are the quarries not far from Pretoria, South Africa, where great pits have been blasted in the ground. Many precious ores are present in such quarries, but great rocks have to be lifted to the rim, crushed into smaller pieces, and separated. Some pieces are shaken and washed so that heavy minerals are trapped by streams of whirling water while others accumulate on the insides of the tables where the sorting is done. Sometimes a flash is seen against the dull background. This specimen is caught in the next step of the sorting process, where it sticks to a specially prepared greasy surface. There the diamonds are collected. It has been estimated that a ton of stone must be dug, crushed, ground fine, rotated, and washed in order to obtain one diamond the size of a pea. And it may be one of poor quality. Or it may be a flawless gem.

Some mining is especially risky. Uranium, the fuel for atomic power reactors, is never found all by itself, and usually it is mixed with large amounts of waste rock. In addition to the difficulty of finding worthwhile deposits, today's uranium miners must be aware of the dangers of breathing radioactive dust.

One of the most important treasures in the earth's crust is "black gold," or petroleum. Over two

Diamonds stick to a grease table; a worker separates them

million oil wells, some as deep as four miles, have helped provide the energy for today's machines. Geologists who study the earth's crust are very important to the petroleum industry. Teams of them are scattered around the world from the cold of Alaska to the steaming jungles near the Equator and the burning sands of the deserts.

If it were not for the restlessness of the earth's crust, men would not be gathering billions of barrels of oil and gas from its underground pockets. Many scientists believe that oil and gas were formed from the remains of plants and animals that fell to the floor of the ocean and were covered by sediments millions of years ago. The decaying organic matter was changed by bacterial action while it was covered by mud and sand, which pressed harder and harder as it became deeper through the years. Layers of hard sedimentary rock formed

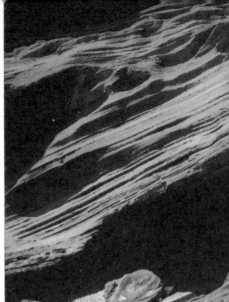

above the porous rock, which contains spaces between the mineral grains, and sealed in the oil and gas. So sediments on the earth's crust trapped these treasures for which men now dig.

The Active Earth

Certainly, continuous movement shapes the crust of the earth. Dramatic forces, such as earthquakes and volcanoes, are discussed later in this book. Slower, less obvious movement is taking place too. In Europe studies of ground level have shown steady trends of rising and falling in various large areas of land in a motion somewhat like a wave crossing an ocean but much slower. The land wave that is slowly crossing Europe could create a new mountain range within a few million years in the area of the central European plain.

Measurements in the United States show that the western coast

Pipelines carry crude oil to waiting tankers

has risen an average of two feet, while the eastern coast has sunk about four inches in recent decades. There are exceptions, such as San Jose, California, which subsided more than eleven feet in about fifty-five years.

In Mexico City sinking is a serious problem, for the rate has reached about nine inches a year. A large part of the city is built on an old lake bed. When buildings were light and the subsoil water was intact, things went well. But heavy buildings and increased drilling of water wells is undermining the city.

Venice, Italy, is another city that is gradually sinking. Venice is built on wooden piles driven into the mud of several hundred tiny islands. Thousands of canals separate its buildings, making it one of the most beautiful and unusual cities in the world. Man, by making the canals, has made the islands more subject to erosion by tides that move sand from one place to another.

The earth is covered with various types of rocks and soils; from left to right, strata of soil, eroded lava, and chalk

Venice, a city of waterways, is slowly sinking into the sea

Engineers have been testing this soil

While Venice looks for a comprehensive plan of rehabilitation, men around the world look to scientists for a better knowledge of the earth on which they live in order to cope with many crises brought about by nature and by the changes of civilization.

For example, in Florida there is a growing problem of sink holes. In one instance two cars dropped to the bottom of a thirty-foot hole that developed so fast that the drivers could not avoid it. A number of such holes have formed as a natural by-product of unusually dry weather in an area where the ground is formed mostly of porous limestone. Water, which picks up carbon dioxide from the air, makes a weak solution of carbonic acid. When the water flows through the underground streams, it dissolves some of the limestone and creates cavities and fractures. When the streams dry up, the limestone may drop into some of these holes, forming sink holes.

The slow sinking of cities, the rising of large areas of the earth, the violent action of earthquakes and volcanoes, and the changes all over the face of the earth are subjects about which there are still many unanswered questions. Scientists change their opinions and theories in the light of new evidence. In spite of the long time men have been studying the earth, there are still many secrets hidden. This is true even of the crust, on which man lives and which he can investigate first-hand.

Houses occasionally fall into Florida sink holes

KNIFE FISH

Black African
Africa
7"

LEAF
FISH

Arapaima
South America
140"-160"

Africa
3"

South
America
3"

PERCH CICHLID
South America
22"

LUNG FISH
South America
40"-50"

PEACOCK
CICHLID
West Africa
3-4"

FRESH WATER
ANGEL FISH
Cichlid Family
Africa & South America
6"

DISCUS FISH
Cichlid Family
Africa & South America
7"

LUNG
FISH

LUNG FISH
Africa
19"-70"

CHAPTER IV

ARE THE
CONTINENTS DRIFTING?

Can you believe that the continents of the earth are slowly moving about on a plasticlike rock in the underlying mantle? Some scientists have suggested that at one time Boston, Massachusetts, which is now in the northern part of the United States, was at the southern icecap not far from the South Pole. Is it possible that the present continents were once part of one or two large supercontinents that have broken apart and drifted over the earth into their present positions? Might they still be drifting?

Some years ago, about 1912, Alfred Wegener proposed the theory of the drifting continents, but many geologists laughed at the idea and considered it pure fantasy. Today, new evidence is making scientists reconsider. Many believe, for example, that New England, now part of the United States, might once have been part of Europe and that those who support the idea of drifting continents might be right. There are many variations in the theories of floating lands and many theories that contradict this idea, but new information is providing excitement.

In the spring of 1967, Dr. J. Tuzo Wilson spoke at a meeting of the American Geophysical Union. He is a noted geophysicist from the University of Toronto who champions the continental drift theory. Dr. Wilson suggested that human beings on drifting continents may be like sailors on a ship, who walk up and down with their eyes on deck, unaware of the motion of the ship. So little is really known about the exciting changes taking place within the earth that Dr. Wilson compared this phase of geology with the time in medicine before 1628, when William Harvey discovered the circulation of blood in the human body.

It has long been noted that some continents seem to fit together like pieces of a jigsaw puzzle. For example, the east coastline of South America fits nicely into the west coastline of Africa. The coasts of Europe and the United States can be made to fit if they are twisted, as pieces are twisted to fit into their places in a jigsaw puzzle. If it is true that continents were broken apart hundreds of millions of years ago, they might have twisted in the process. Even more important in support of the continental drift theory may be the fact that the mountain ranges that face each other across oceans can be matched by geological age and rock structure.

Many expert botanists believe that plants could not be distributed

The similarity of fresh water fish supports the theory that the continents were united

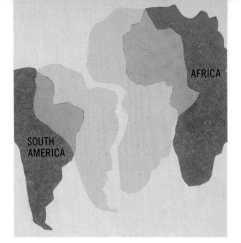

If pushed together, the coastlines of South America and Africa would match each other

throughout the world the way they are if the continents had not been joined together in some way in the past. There is also some support from zoologists, who note that fish and other fresh water creatures in Africa have close relatives across the sea in South America and that certain giant lizards that lay their eggs in termite nests are found wild only in South America and Africa. These are just a few of the reasons many feel that the two continents were once linked.

The recent excitement about the continental drift theory is due in part to a new branch of geophysics called paleomagnetism. It is the study of magnetic lines of force in ancient rocks. Everyone knows that there is a North and a South Pole, and many people believe that a compass needle points to the North Pole. Actually, the whole earth acts like a huge magnet, and the compass needle points to the magnetic north pole. It does not, however, always point exactly to the magnetic north pole, which is hundreds of miles south of the geographic North Pole. The direction in which a compass needle points varies at different places on the earth. And to make matters more complicated, the magnetic north and south poles wander about through the years.

Scientists aren't even sure why the earth behaves like a magnet, but they know that the old theory of the

iron center of the earth is not the reason. The heat at the core would destroy magnetism in the iron. Many scientists believe that the earth's motion makes it behave somewhat like a dynamo in a power plant, in which the turning of a core of iron sets up a magnetic field. In much the same way electric current flowing through the core of the earth may be responsible for the magnetic field around the earth.

When hot lava or liquid magma cools, various iron-bearing minerals in the rock cool enough to retain magnetic properties. When the rock hardens, the tiny magnetic particles are frozen, pointing to the magnetic poles of the earth. Recently, ribbons of magnetized rocks were discovered on the floor of the ocean; their magnetic lines of force pointed in different directions. This evidence seems to support the continental drift theory.

The Drifting Poles

Over periods of thousands or even millions of years, the north and south magnetic poles have traveled so much that they have even, at times, been in opposite positions. Such a reversal of the poles has been proven by magnetic records in rocks. Scientists can read this magnetic calendar because they can determine the age of rocks through modern dating methods. If such a magnetic reversal were to take place overnight, you would find the needle of your compass pointing in the opposite direction. Most scientists believe that the movement of magnetic poles is very slow. In the case of the ribbons of rock on the ocean floor, it was found that the poles alternated in each ribbon. Hot rock from the mid-ocean ridges recorded the orientation of the rocks in relation to the poles

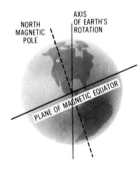

NORTH MAGNETIC POLE

AXIS OF EARTH'S ROTATION

PLANE OF MAGNETIC EQUATOR

The magnetic poles of the earth do not lie exactly north and south

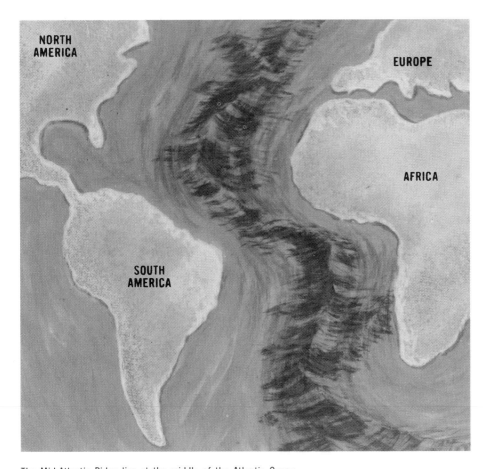

The Mid-Atlantic Ridge lies at the middle of the Atlantic Ocean

and shows reversals. Rocks from continents also show that they have been oriented to the poles differently from their present positions. Much information comparing the position of poles at various dates with positions of land gives evidence that both poles and land have changed in relation to each other.

The mid-ocean system of ridges itself gives support to the continental drift theory in either one of two possible ways. Some scientists believe that ridges and rifts on the ocean floor are evidence that the earth might be expanding. If the earth is expanding, this expansion may be what caused the splitting of the continents.

If the earth is not expanding—and many scientists claim it is not—the rifts might support the drift theory in another way. They might be places where circular rolling currents of plastic material flowed to the underside of the continents and made them break apart, build mountains, sustain earthquakes, and so on. Of course, no one really knows.

Opponents of the Drift Theory

There are still many opponents of the continental drift theory, including Sir Harold Jeffreys, a famous British geophysicist. He believes that the earth is quite stable and solid down to the core and much too rigid to allow such movements of large masses as would be the case

if continents are moving over the mantle.

Some scientists believe that the interior of the earth has some elasticity but is basically twice as rigid as steel. Another objection to the drift theory is the fact that the earth's crust between rift valleys seems to be opening in both directions, rather than in just one direction. Others include the fact that some measurements seem to indicate that the radius of the earth has not varied more than a few miles in the last 200 million years. If such is the case, the earth seems quite stable.

Scientists work in many ways to try to answer the questions of what is happening beneath the rocky crust. Egan Orowan, a physicist at the Massachusetts Institute of Technology in the United States, has an interesting theory about drifting continents. He experimented with a substance called polycrystalline alumina, which he used to imitate the materials in the upper mantle and crust of the earth. From his experiments with heat currents in this material, he concluded that heat currents in the earth could start a slow, plastic flow, a hot creep, in which crystals slide on one another. He calculates that the United States is drifting westward at a rate of about one third of an inch a year.

Other geologists have calculated that the ocean floors must be flowing away from the ridges near

Dogs pull sleds loaded with scientific equipment across the rough terrain of Antarctica

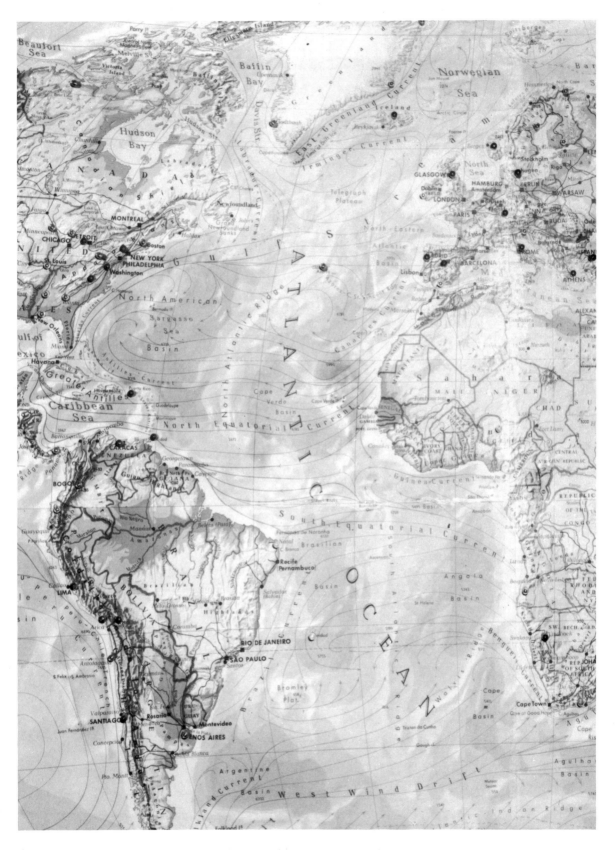

46

the center of the oceans at a speed of about one inch per year, so that the continents of Europe and America are drifting apart. Such ideas are not wild guesses but the result of the work of learned men who experiment, test theories, and draw conclusions in the light of the best available evidence. Some dig in the dusty or rocky earth.

Aboard the *Oceanographer*

Imagine joining a group of geologists from the United States and Australia who are conducting an extensive survey to test the soundness of the continental drift theory. You will sail on a ten-million-dollar floating laboratory, a United States Coast Guard and Geological Survey ship called the *Oceanographer,* using instruments so modern that you will navigate by satellite.

As you sail along, echo soundings will be taken to survey the continental slope; special note will be made of the contour line at a thousand fathoms (6,000 feet). Soundings will be made that reach deep into the floor of the ocean to determine the geological structure below the sea bottom. Continuous readings will be made of the forces of gravity and magnetism.

As your ship rolls and pitches over the submerged slopes off western and southern Australia, the information it gathers will help answer questions about the possibility of the existence of two supercontinents, Gondwana and Laurasia. Dr. Robert S. Dietz, who is in charge of the survey, believes that Gondwana was composed of Australia, Antarctica, India, South America, Africa, Malagasy, and various submerged fragments. Laurasia may have been what is

The pin heads on this section of a world map locate seismograph stations around the world. They all cooperate with the U.S. Coast and Geodetic Survey

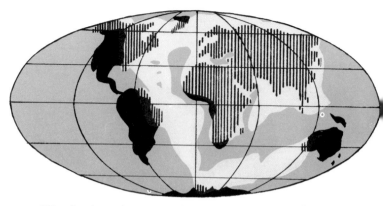

Gondwana, a supposed ancient continent is shown in light blue. Today's continents, in black, probably drifted apart from it

now North America and Eurasia. Antarctica's Wilkes Land (where McMurdo Base is located) once fit into the Great Bight of Australia, and the island of Tasmania, off Australia's southeastern coast, fitted snugly into the Ross Sea. Today, the two ancient continents are separated by about 2,000 miles of ocean.

Such a survey took place on the *Oceanographer* during the summer of 1967. It was one of many surveys taken around the world to learn more about the structure of the earth in years long past. Why spend all this time and money trying to answer questions about conditions on the earth millions of years ago? It may be interesting, but what good will it do?

The solution of the continental drift theory would provide a better understanding of the earth's structure, helping to fit pieces of a global jigsaw puzzle into place. With better understanding of how the earth was formed, geologists can better help those who will inherit the earth in the future.

The fascinating science of modern geology is helping to fill in some of the clues to the puzzles of the earth's crust and what lies beneath it. Among other things, it is helping to predict earthquakes and volcanoes, violent actions that are brought about by mysterious stirrings deep in the earth.

47

CHAPTER V

NEW IDEAS
ABOUT EARTHQUAKES

In Matsushiro, Japan, a small town about one hundred miles north of Tokyo, people wake up night after night because the earth trembles beneath them. Between August of 1965 and December of 1966, more than 565,000 earthquakes were recorded in that town. One day 661 earthquake shocks were felt by people, almost 7,000 were recorded by instruments, and three hundred homes were damaged. It is not surprising that many buildings have suffered from the tremors that come again and again.

Living in Matsushiro is an uneasy sort of life. Who knows what will happen next? Some of the people are so frightened by the frequent shaking that they take refuge in open fields when the trembling is strong. Some say the "gods" are angry because scientists have set up instruments near the religious shrine on Mount Minakami. Even the scientists do not know what is really happening or why. Some think the shocks will soon stop, while others wonder if the earth is building up to a major earthquake.

Earthquakes are far more common than most people realize. You may have been in the area of a minor one and not even realized it. More than a million earthquakes occur around the world in a single year, but only about 700 are strong enough to cause considerable damage. Most originate beneath the sea, where they harm no one unless they are large enough to set up "tidal waves," or *tsunami*.

Perhaps you remember seeing pictures of the tremendous earthquake in Alaska. On March 27, 1964, a rock slippage took place about eighteen miles under the surface of the earth in that part of the world. This action shook an area of hundreds of thousands of square miles. Even as far away as Florida the water level in wells dropped several feet. In Alaska, at the focal point of the quake, the land shook for as long as four minutes.

Imagine the horror of seeing houses fall into a great crack in the street. Strange and terrible sights were everywhere. Here and there a house remained standing, while neighboring houses were twisted apart. Great lengths of concrete highway were torn apart. Concrete slabs were piled together like shingles on a roof. Two small boys who were playing in their yard suddenly disappeared into a crevasse that opened in the earth's crust.

Along the shore the first *tsunami*, a wave caused by the major shock, rolled in thirty feet high, Land-

Severe earthquakes can cause extensive damage

This series of photographs shows a house collapsing during an earthquake

slides under the water caused even larger waves, which dashed against the shore destroying fishing villages and canning factories. Whole towns along the coast were destroyed over a large area, and there was some havoc as far south as California. In one night the loss in lives reached about 115, and the loss in property was 350 million dollars. Homeless and injured added to the toll.

Tragedy and earthquakes have stalked hand in hand through the centuries, causing far more devastation in some parts of the world than in others. If you live along the mountainous rim of the Pacific Ocean, you may have a very personal interest in earthquakes, for this zone is especially active. The same is true if you live in the southern portion of Europe or Asia. The four humps mentioned in the first chapter of this book seem to be especially prone to earthquakes.

Earthquakes may be as old as the earth itself, but it is just recently that scientists have had the instruments and cooperation necessary to begin an all-out attack on the problem.

The Causes of Earthquakes

Today's scientists are making an international effort to learn more about the causes of quakes and to find better methods of prediction and ways to protect people and their property against them. Although they already know something of the causes and they can identify earthquakes around the world by instruments, the exact causes are still being debated. In fact, there are so many new findings, new theories, and new methods of learning about the earth that geology is sometimes thought of as a science in a state of revolution. Old textbooks no longer

tell the story of the earth in the light of new knowledge. So it is with the study of earthquakes.

One point on which geologists agree is that strong earthquakes are due, in most cases, to the rupturing of great masses of rock many miles beneath the surface of the earth. Rock masses slip and slide along a rupture plane, which is called a fault. Great blocks of rock perhaps ten miles wide, may undergo a tilting process, and the fault may be as much as fifty feet high. It is easy to see why the earth above trembles, causing catastrophe to large areas.

A *tsunami* is due to a sudden rising or dropping of the ocean floor. You might be traveling in a ship at sea where the water is quite deep when far below you rocks slip and a rift opens in the bed of the ocean. Your ship might be carried ashore by the tremendous wave that results from such an earthquake, but it is more likely that you would be totally unaware of any change at all, because the distance between crests of such waves is often as far apart as one hundred miles.

In some areas where destructive waves roll ashore with unusual fre-quency, natives race for the hills as soon as strong shocks are felt along the coast.

The prediction of major earthquakes could save much destruction. Earthquake studies are based mainly on shock waves in the earth's interior. Scientists have measured shock waves caused by the vibrations that are set up when rocks fracture along a fault. They have done this with some precision for more than fifty years. The study of these waves is known as the science of seismology, and the instruments used are known as

Rocks moving along a fault cause water in the ocean to form *tsunami*

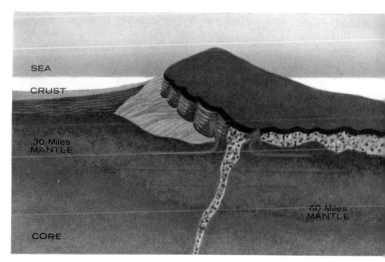

SEA

CRUST

30 Miles
MANTLE

60 Miles
MANTLE

CORE

Earthquakes are recorded on seismographs

seismographs. They can register vibrations far from their source, while the vibrations from a large earthquake set up waves that penetrate through the entire structure of the earth and travel all over its surface.

A seismograph is basically a delicately balanced weight or pendulum, which is suspended in a firm frame on bedrock. It transmits and records electrically the wave motions of the earth, which moves under the pendulum. The motions can be interpreted by scientists. A scientist in Italy can tell much about what is happening in Japan. A scientist in France can tell what is happening in Alaska. The recordings of seismographs indicate directions, travel times, reflections, speed, and other information that helps pinpoint the size and time of earthquakes around the world.

Types of Earthquakes

The major types of earthquake waves are divided into two kinds: P (or push) waves, which move like a coiled spring when a spring is pushed back and forth, and S (or shake) waves, which move like a coiled spring when you shake it sideways. As one would guess, surface waves are those that travel along the surface of the earth, somewhat like the waves that move along a rope fixed at one end and shaken at the other. The behavior of these waves in different types of material helps paint the following picture of the inside of the earth.

It is the real beginning of earthquake science.

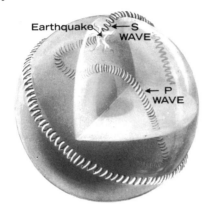

Shock waves from earthquakes move through the earth like waves through springs; S waves move like those shown in the left-hand spring and P waves move like those in the right-hand spring

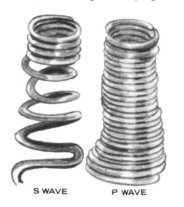

S WAVE   P WAVE

The Earth's Interior

The earth's crust, discussed in the last chapter, has been compared to an apple's skin. But when one thinks of a ball with a diameter of 8,000 miles and a crust about twenty-two to thirty-seven miles thick on the continents and only three to four and a half miles thick under the oceans, even an apple's skin is thick by comparison.

Below the crust there is a transition layer between the crust and the deep earth where seismic waves jump suddenly in velocity. This is the famous Mohorovicic discontinuity, which was named for its discoverer, the Croatian seismologist Andrija Mohorovicic. The Moho, as it is nicknamed, is the upper limit of the mantle, which is probably a dark, dense basaltic rock somewhat like the rock known as olivine. The mantle is about 1,800 miles deep, and beneath it is the core. How do we know? Earthquake waves have been compared with the action of similar waves on various kinds of material in laboratories, and the material of the mantle causes little disagreement among geologists.

What is it like in the core of the earth? Scientists still dispute this question, although many feel certain that the core is probably made of iron and nickel. Earthquake waves indicate an outer core of liquid or molten nickel-iron and possibly a solid nickel-iron center. In any case, the core is believed to be very dense and very hot. Recent estimates of the core's temperature have reduced it from a possible 13,500 degrees Fahrenheit to only 6,700 degrees Fahrenheit. In any case, it is very hot.

Much as one hand washes the other, knowledge gained from earthquake waves helps scientists learn more about the deep part of the earth, and knowledge about the deep part of the earth helps scientists learn about earthquakes. That is one of the reasons that scientists have begun digging deep into the earth in a number of parts of the world.

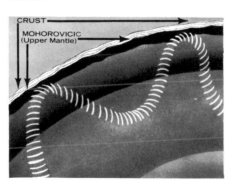

CRUST
MOHOROVICIC
(Upper Mantle)

Earthquake waves move faster below the Mohorovicic layer

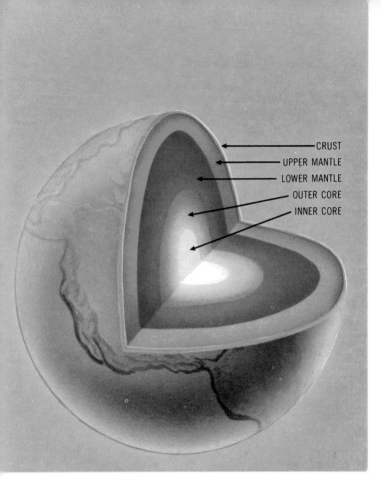

The earth is made up of many layers

CRUST
UPPER MANTLE
LOWER MANTLE
OUTER CORE
INNER CORE

Mohole

Early in 1961 scientists in the United States began an exciting project in which they hoped to drill a hole through the earth's crust into the mantle that lies below it. They named the project Mohole, for they planned to penetrate the boundary between the crust and the mantle, the Moho. It was easy to nickname a hole in the Moho as Mohole. But the naming was far easier than the digging.

The Moho lies eighteen to thirty miles below land surfaces but only three to six miles below the ocean floor. For this reason, the site chosen for test drills was under the sea. The problems of drilling through three miles of rock beneath five or six miles of water, were great indeed. Men have drilled oil wells about five miles deep on land, but since the underlying crust is so much deeper on land, drilling platforms at sea seemed comparatively easy.

Imagine how drillers lowered into the water a 3,500-foot pipe, tipped with a diamond-toothed, doughnut-shaped drilling bit that could bite deeply into the ocean floor. At various depths in the drilling a twenty-foot-long core barrel was dropped in the pipe to trap a cylindrical core of material, which a cable brought back to the drilling platform for examination. When such a core barrel came up inside the long polished tube, scientists handled it almost reverently, for men had seldom sampled the ocean floor more deeply than sixty feet.

During one experimental drilling a basalt core sample from six hundred feet below the sea floor was recovered; it was polished, and put on exhibit in the Smithsonian Institution in Washington, D.C. But Mohole was plagued with troubles, and the initial budget was raised. Unfortunately, even the new financial support was not enough, and the project had to be abandoned for budget reasons.

Other drilling programs are continuing in various parts of the world under a recent program that eight nations have joined. Scientists are probing the earth to gain more knowledge about many things, in addition to the problem of earthquakes. The International Upper Mantle Project has sponsored many deep-drilling investigations.

Scientists suspect that an area of land that lies along the border between Germany and France may go right through the crust into the upper mantle. Russia reports that a drilling operation is underway near the north shore of the Caspian Sea, where it is hoped that they may reach a depth of four and a half miles. There is much activity in

Canada, where the Canadian Upper Mantle Committee is sponsoring many projects and publishing the proceedings of meetings held recently to bring together the information gathered by scientists in many countries.

How the Earth Moves

Drilling is just one of the many approaches to learning more about the interior of the earth and the problems of earthquakes. From the Arctic to Antarctica, from the holes deep in the earth to information sent back from satellites in outer space, the search for earthquake prediction methods goes on. Although few geologists question that earthquakes begin underground and that a fault is involved, they differ on basic causes. Some believe that heat causes expansion of the rock of the earth and the resulting stretching of the crust causes them. Some believe that molecular changes in rock due to temperature and pressure variations are major contributing causes. On one thing there is agreement: no one knows all the answers. More knowledge is needed before man can really do much about prediction.

In March of 1967 the Environmental Science Services Administration (ESSA) of the United States announced the establishment of an effective exchange system of scientific data for earthquake research, with almost seventy countries cooperating. Reports from seismologists arrive daily at the National Earthquake Information Center, Rockville, Maryland, from such distant points as Greenland, Antarctica, Hong Kong, the Fiji Islands, and the Congo. Data from hundreds of thousands of observations, which is sorted and processed by computers,

is made available to cooperating scientists.

One important approach to earthquake research is the accurate location of the precise point at which an earthquake was centered. Twenty or more seismological stations must report for ideal plotting, and they must be distributed around the earth. With this information, the search for information needed to establish an advance-warning system is just beginning.

Measuring the Shifting Ground

Suppose you are a scientist in the field, working on one phase of research in an effort to add clues to help solve the mystery of earthquakes. You are stationed in California, working along the San Andreas fault, which is a crack in

A laser Geodimeter is adjusted by a surveyor

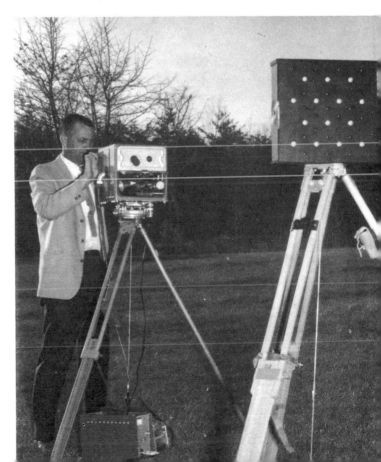

the earth's crust that runs from north of San Francisco to Mexico. It is the longest visible fault and is famous as the cause of the San Francisco earthquake of 1906. You are stationed at one of the ten "clusters"—areas where instruments are concentrated—along the fault line, where you work with devices that are capable of measuring microscopic changes in an area where change in the earth's crust is comparatively rapid. It has been estimated that the city of Los Angeles is moving northward at the rate of fifteen feet per hundred years, and the movement along the fault itself is between one and two inches in a single year.

In one experiment a laser beam is used to measure changes in the amount of strain in the rockbed. It can determine microscopic amounts of expansion and contraction in rock and thus determine earth movements of less than a millionth of a centimeter. Each small change may help to signal a buildup in strain in the earth's crust.

A laser produces an extremely intense and narrow beam of light that can be used as a measuring device for distance, somewhat the way radar is used. One beam of light travels across the fault to a mirror about twelve miles away and is reflected back again. A similar beam travels an equal distance, is reflected by a mirror, and returns,

Laser beam photographed at distance of 10 miles from position of geodimeter

but it does not cross the fault. If there is no motion, the rays return in the same time. If there is even the slightest movement along the fault, the rays return at different times, and there is evidence of very slight rock shifts or strain increase.

In another experiment, a laser strain meter tells you more about what is happening. Laser beams are made to shine through pipes that are buried in the ground; air has been removed from the pipes so that weather conditions will not affect the experiment. Each pipe is about a half mile long. There are a number of them laid out in various directions. Strain in the rocks will be indicated by differences in the measure of the beam caused by squeezing pressures of rock.

There are other instruments that must be monitored at your "cluster," including those that measure gravity and the magnetic field. Some devices measure changes in the tilt of the rock, while still others measure shock waves with seismographs. Today's seismographs can detect a change in the ground's position as small as three one hundred millionths of an inch.

In such a research station you would be one of many scientists working around the world to speed the day when warning signals can prevent death and destruction from large and small tremors in the earth. So much must be learned that the time of accurate predictions may be far away. In the meantime, scientists and engineers are working on constructing buildings to withstand stress and strain better when earthquakes do occur.

Earthquakes to Order

Imagine making "earthquakes to order" in an attempt to test the strength of a skyscraper. In Cali-

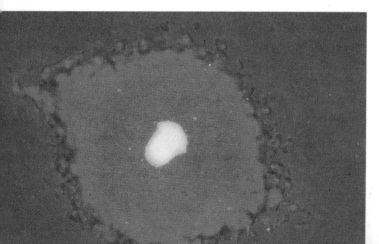

fornia men are producing artificial earthquakes or vibrations similar to those caused by a trembling earth, and they are testing buildings to see whether the framework is strong enough to withstand a natural earthquake. Some machines, vibration generators, can shake the building up and down or from side to side.

At Lehigh University, in Bethlehem, Pennsylvania, scientists are testing the endurance of steel columns and beams in model buildings that can be built so that they are more shock-absorbing. The three story steel frame is being very, very slowly pushed back and forth to learn more about its behavior under stress. At first this research was applicable to buildings of just a few stories, but today it is being applied to buildings up to twenty or thirty stories high.

Soils that are largely composed of silt or clay are easily washed away and are poor foundations for homes. Such soils are subject to landslide, so if homes must be built on them, special shoring, drainage, and soil conditioning should be arranged. That is something that can be done about earthquakes without waiting for scientists to find out more about their causes.

Although most earthquakes occur in the "rings of fire," or well-defined earthquake zones, one could happen at any part of the earth. While waiting for a warning system to be developed, those who have been through earthquakes offer advice about what to do when one strikes. Some suggest standing in doorways. Some suggest taking to the fields. Some say to climb under a bed; others say to meditate. Even though you live in an earthquake zone, there is relatively little danger that one will harm you. In any case, there seems to be as much disagreement about what to do when an earthquake strikes as there is about why they occur. But one thing is certain. When scientists learn more about the deep part of the earth, they will have a better chance of warning people to leave before an earthquake strikes.

Earthquake areas of the world occur near the continental shores

Engineers push light beams back and forth to test them against earthquake shocks

57

CHAPTER VI

EXPLORING
GLACIAL ICE
AND DESERT SANDS

Some futurists picture millions of square miles of sandy desert changing to blooming farmlands and gleaming cities for the exploding population of the earth. Such changes have already started in Israel and the southwestern United States. A team of scientists in the far north is trying to push back the frontiers of living space by studying permafrost, or permanently frozen subsoil. A delicate thermal balance results in severe ground settling when foundations are laid for building and the equilibrium is disturbed. For many years men have talked of blocking cold sea currents with dams in order to unfreeze Arctic ports. Deserts, both hot and cold, are a great challenge to the scientists trying to stretch the resources of the earth.

Perhaps you have never thought of a glacier as a desert. Large glaciers and icecaps are mostly lifeless and deserted, and the word *desert* comes from a Latin word that means abandoned. So in the true sense, they too are deserts. Certainly, they are largely wasteland on an earth that is becoming increasingly crowded.

Deserts have been described as the last frontier for privacy. In the sweep of technological revolution, sandy deserts and the earth beneath

the blue ice of glaciers are land and mineral banks from which man may draw for his future needs. They are two unique faces of the planet earth, and they are more vast than most people realize. One square mile in seven is desert today. Antarctica alone contains seven million cubic miles of ice and snow. Although large amounts of melted ice and snow may never be used to make dry deserts flourish, there are towns such as Boulder, Colorado, that today get some of their water supply from the melting ice and snow of glaciers.

The striking beauty of glacial ice and desert sands fascinates many people, and many myths surround these strange parts of the world. Much remains to be learned about these areas. They are natural laboratories that men are barely beginning to use.

Today's scientists are helping to uncloak the mysteries of deserts and glaciers for a number of reasons. New and better instruments provide new windows into hidden areas of science. For example, in polar regions ski planes and helicopters bring loads of supplies to areas so men can penetrate far from civilization and still carry on sophisticated experiments. Needs for more mineral resources, more living

Natural ice crystals form beautiful shapes

Geologists explore a mountain glacier

space, and more information about the earth and an appreciation of the interdependence of all parts of the earth have helped stimulate interest in deserts.

An Alpine Glacier

Suppose you are an earth scientist who has volunteered to join a team of explorers who are setting out for a station in France to study Alpine glaciers. Mer de Glace, for example, is a beautiful mass of blue ice that is slowly moving down the mountains in the region of Chamonix and Mount Blanc. There tourists ride the cog railway to the glacier from the town nestled in the valley. They transfer to a *téléférique,* or cable car, for the rest of the journey. Day after day, tourists walk along the narrow path that leads to the apartment of ice built inside the glacier. One cannot see much at the front door or even from the apartment roof. The whole unit is concealed beneath the massive ice sheet that encompasses it.

Visitors walk down the long hall, where a trough catches the water as

it drips through the roof of melting snow and ice. Many feet inside, one can sit in the ice chairs of the dining room, look about the cold kitchen-of-ice, visit the bedroom carved from ice, and even have a picture taken inside the glacier apartment. Amid all the ice, the air is comfortably cool in summer. The dripping from the bit that melts is indeed imperceptible when one considers the whole glacier.

While streams of tourists enjoy the sights, you are busy with your instruments, recording various information such as temperature, motion of snow and ice, pressure of the air, and other weather phenomena. Slowly the glacier creeps down the mountain. You collect and interpret data that add to the great quest for understanding of the vast and alien world of snow and ice.

The Vast Antarctica

As a glaciologist, one might spend a summer in Antarctica, an international natural laboratory where many scientists are continually searching for secrets of ice, snow, rock formations, bird naviga-

Penguins are the largest land animals in Antarctica

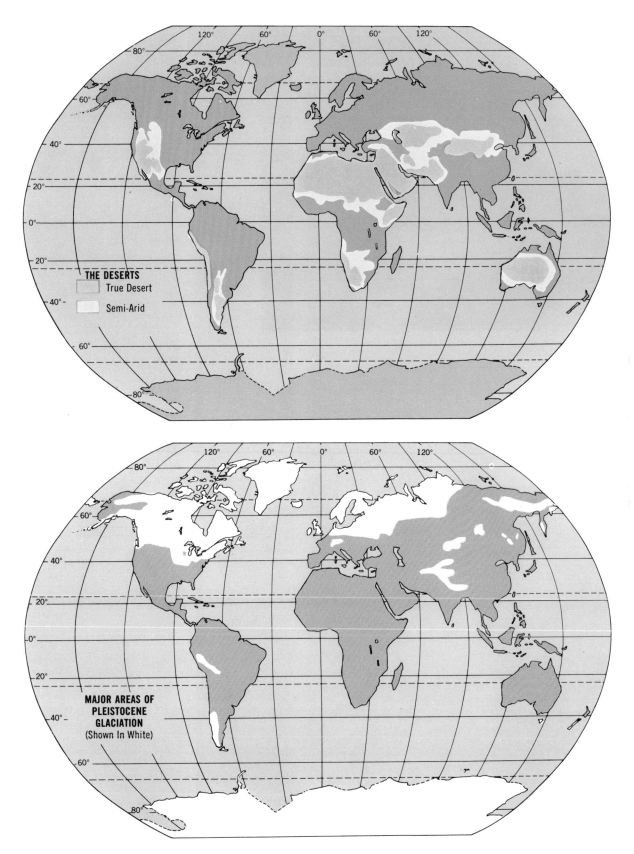

THE DESERTS
True Desert
Semi-Arid

MAJOR AREAS OF
PLEISTOCENE
GLACIATION
(Shown In White)

61

Huge icebergs can threaten ship lanes

point, regardless of the weather ahead.

Icebergs are a beautiful sight in the waters beneath the plane. They are huge islands of ice that have broken away from the glacier. The view of Victoria Land, which lies ahead, is breathtaking, with its white mountains protruding above the ice and snow in majestic silence. The plane can put down on an ice shelf about fifty feet inland, using skis rather than wheels. Helicopters are waiting for it and, what seems more important to those who greet the plane than the passengers, the mail.

Life in Antarctica

Life in Antarctica is a great experiment in international living, for there men from a dozen nations work together toward the goal of learning more about the earth on which they live. They put up with numerous hardships in an unbelievably lonely place, for in spite of the influx of scientists and the establishment of new stations, life is scarce in the vastness of Antarctica. The United States has recently established Plateau Station at what is believed to be the coldest spot on earth. Here, about 600 miles northeast of the South Pole, the temperature drops to 130 degrees or more below zero Fahrenheit.

Still, some men go to these barren and isolated places with dedication. Some explore areas where men have never before set foot, as they probe the secrets of Antarctica. One experiment is a search for tillite, rock that appears to have been formed from gravel left by

tion, atmospheric disturbances, mineral wealth, and many other things. The plane leaves from a famous gateway to Antarctica, Christchurch, New Zealand, in October, since the summer months there are opposite to the ones in Europe and the United States. The giant transport plane is equipped with skis and wheels so that it can land on whatever surface it finds at its destination. The load it carries is more cargo than men, for the two dozen passengers and the "luggage" weigh three tons.

It takes eight hours for the plane to cross the 2,280 miles of hostile sea and land. After just four hours of flying time, one can notice the beautiful deep blue below, where the cold waters slip under the warm waters from the north. This is the famous Antarctic Convergence, where the churning waters have brought rich mineral water to the surface and the sea is rich in living things, perhaps richer, acre for acre, than in any other part of the world. This is often called the point of no return, for one continues to Antarctica if one has reached this

Ice Ages occurred at different times in the past; many glaciers covered lands that are now free of ice

glaciers several hundred million years ago. Tillite from Antarctica can be compared with tillite from far away lands, perhaps to help support the idea of the supercontinents mentioned on page 46. If tillite from Antarctica matches tillite found in Australia, India, and distant lands, this information may add another clue to the unsolved puzzle of the continental drift.

The Antarctic glacier is one of the major features of the earth, for it is 2,500 miles across and an average of over a mile thick. If all this ice were to melt, it might raise the level of the world's oceans as much as two hundred feet. Is the glacier melting or increasing? This is just another of the many problems scientists are studying.

What Snow Reveals

Beneath the surface of the snow, men can uncover traces of events that took place thousands of years ago. The work in Antarctica may be far-reaching both in time and in the areas in which it is studied. Suppose a glaciologist is assigned to gathering ice core samples to be shipped to Hanover, New Hampshire, where the Cold Regions Research and Engineering Laboratory will compare them with ice cores from other parts of the world. Some of the deep ice-core drilling is done with a well-drilling rig that can bring back sections from about nine hundred feet beneath the surface. In some areas men work in "snow mines," which are tunnels many feet below the surface. The instruments are installed at several levels in the mine, and men drill cores from different regions. There is a workroom in the snow mine where they store and examine samples. They need not worry about melting, for the temperature is

FALLING SNOW

ICE CRYSTALS

COMPRESSED CRYSTALS

FLOWING CRYSTALS

CRUST

Glaciers are made up of various types of snow and ice

Helicopters fly to the most remote areas to bring supplies to scientists studying glaciers

naturally about 60 degrees below zero Fahrenheit.

In collecting ice cores, glaciologists can label layers of snow and ice according to the year in which they were originally laid down. And they can read the age of ice cores by layers, somewhat the way one can read the age of a tree by the rings in its trunk. Each layer was formed by the refreezing of summer melt water. Air bubbles are trapped in the layers and they enable scientists to tell what the atmosphere was like when the ice froze. They can also examine dust and volcanic ash trapped there. It is possible that information gained from the study of glacial ice may help man to plot climate centuries ahead because it reveals patterns of climate change. The cores men have dug in Antarctica and the other work they have begun may reach the laboratories of scientists in far parts of the world long after they have left the cold continent.

Not long ago a cargo of ice worth one million dollars reached Hanover, New Hampshire, in a trailer truck in which the temperature was minus twenty degrees Fahrenheit. The scientists who greeted the truck did so with excitement and apprehension. The 20,000 pounds of ice was an accumulation of the work of men from pole to pole who had endured many hardships at great expense to the governments and scientific societies who had sent them. Had the ice endured the trip? No wonder there was cheering when the boxes were broken open and the ice was hard.

Glaciers Around the World

Glaciologists around the world are studying the problem of how glaciers form and how they move. These rivers of ice begin with the tiny six-pointed snowflakes that fall in many parts of the world. In some areas, snow piles up faster than it melts. Flakes deep in the accumulation melt slightly because

Snowflakes in glaciers slowly change into ice crystals

65

of the pressure from upper areas, and their shape changes so they become smooth grains of packed snow. Melted snow refreezes at night and during colder spells, and these grains become coarse crystals called firn. Firn is packed together somewhat like a snowball, and as pressure increases, it forms a very hard layer of ice. Layer after layer adds to the pile, and eventually a glacier is formed.

Why and how do glaciers move? This is a question that cannot be completely explained even by the scientists who spend their lives studying glaciers. There are two types of glaciers, and their movement seems to be connected with the type. Continental glaciers are vast ice sheets, the largest of which is in the Antarctic. Greenland has another. Alpine glaciers nestle in the mountains, sometimes shrink-ing, sometimes growing. When two Alpine glaciers meet at the foot of a mountain, they form a piedmont glacier. There are many classifications of glaciers, but no matter what the variety, they all move.

There are various theories about what happens at the under surface of glaciers and about how they move. Some glaciologists believe that the ice of glaciers flows somewhat like tar, because of pressure. Some suggest that the motion of glaciers comes from continual melting and refreezing of ice crystals, which glide over one another somewhat like ball bearings.

Recent news articles about "galloping" glaciers have caused some excitement. In the northwestern part of North America, speeds up to two feet an hour have been observed by scientists of the United States Geological Survey. Normal

A motor toboggan is used in support of the scientific program during "Deep Freeze—63"

A meteorlogist measures snow temperatures at the IGY Little American Station

Since the peak of this ice age is believed to be about 15,000 years away, it is nothing for you to worry about.

Sometimes scientists study the cold part of the earth while living on islands of ice. One ice island, T-3, has been nicknamed the United States Navy's biggest bargain, since it is somewhat like a ship sailing in the Arctic Ocean at the rate of as much as seven miles a day. Actually, it is a chunk of ice about six miles long and three miles wide that broke away from a glacier and has been manned by scientists and U.S. Armed Forces personnel since 1952 except for one year, when it ran aground near Barrow, Alaska. Currents pulled it loose again, and the ship of ice, or iceberg, continues as a research station where men can learn more about this cold and isolated part of the earth.

The Deserts

In both the world of glacial cold and the world of desert heat, there are many amazing phenomena. Strange as it may seem, there is sometimes snow in the tropical deserts, and there are some areas of the polar ones where very little snow falls. But on the whole, the hot sandy deserts are characterized by an extreme lack of water. They are seared by the sun and scoured by the wind to varying degrees; some deserts are drier than others. In fact, the deserts—the ones discussed in the rest of this chapter—differ in many ways, but they all have the common factor of low annual rainfall. In contrast to the glacial deserts, they are typically places of high heat. Much as the cold makes the glacial deserts uninviting homes for most men, the lack of water and the intense heat make

flow rate for these glaciers is about one or two feet a day. Some glaciers in Alaska and Canada have been reported advancing at more than a hundred feet a day. No one knows why this is happening, but these are interesting movements.

Many textbooks discuss four or five definite ages when glaciers crept over large parts of the land that are now quite warm. Some new theories claim that there are more periods when glaciers crept over much of the land. Some claim less. Most of them agree that there is scientific evidence of plant and animal life in Antarctica, which indicates that it once had a tropical climate. While some scientists claim that a warming trend is on its way, others say that the earth is getting colder as another ice age is approaching.

the sandy deserts formidable. Man has learned to respect the dangers of both areas.

The most famous desert in the world, the Sahara, is also the largest in the world. This desert stretches from one side of North Africa to the other, for a distance of about 3,200 miles. It covers an area of more than three and a half million square miles, an area almost as large as the entire United States. In such a vast place there is, of course, great variation. There are mountains and canyons. There are broad stretches of flat sands and larger sections that are rocky. Dunes cover only about 10 percent of the Sahara, and very little is sandy. There are ripples of wind-blown sand that repeat the patterns of larger dunes, with the steep slope of the ripple or dune always away from the prevailing wind direction; and there are beautifully patterned star dunes, where the wind blows from all directions. There are transverse dunes, with ridges made of coarser particles

than those in the valleys between; and there are longitudinal dunes with deep troughs parallel to the wind direction. There is simplicity of form and repetition of pattern, and there is an almost indescribable beauty in formations of endless variety. But the desert is dry, and the desert is harsh.

The view of a desert is far more inviting than the effect it has on the human body. In the daytime, the temperature in the shade on the Sahara is often 120 degrees on summer days. The sand is often hotter than the air. Such a situation is one that leads to rapid dehydration of the human body. You can lose so much water by perspiring during one day on the desert that you can die by the end of the day if you have no water to replace that given off by your body's cooling mechanism. Even if you were given a ration of a gallon per day, while exposed to the desert sun, you could not last much more than a week.

At night, the desert temperature

may drop about fifty degrees, for there are no rain clouds in the sky to deflect some of the day's accumulation of heat. No plants that provide normal land cover and very few bodies of water are present to affect the temperature as in most places. Water grows hotter or colder more slowly than dry earth, helping to maintain a more even air temperature and helping to hold the heat of day through nightime. Scientists have barely begun to attack the problem of comfortable desert living, even though some people manage to survive in such parts of the world.

Types of Deserts

Ergs are great expanses of sand dunes, the part of a desert that most people picture even though they are only a small percentage of the whole area. There is an erg in the Libyan Desert that is as large as the whole country of France. Standing at the edge of an erg, one views the sea of sand with awe. But if one walks just a little way into the erg, he may be lost within minutes, for he may not even be able to backtrack. One's footprints might be blown beyond recognition in a matter of seconds.

Have you ever thought of a rock desert? Hamadas are a form of desert terrain formed on upland plateaus that are the remains of steep watercourses. The wind blows the sand from some large layers of rock and forms some of the hamadas. The water no longer flows, and the rocks stand like naked skeletons. Some surfaces are stones, some layers of rock, and some shale. Actually, other types of deserts originate from hamadas.

Suppose rain falls on a rocky hamada, as it does on rare occasions. The rain does not soak in, as it would where grass or other plants cover the surface, and slow the flow of the water. Instead, the water gushes off the surfaces, down the slopes, and becomes a torrential flood by the time it reaches a depressed pocket in the desert. Storm after storm, with rushing water that carries masses of stones and silt, eventually builds a type of desert called a reg.

Regs are layers of silt that have been deposited by raging desert rivers over vast areas of land. Wind scours the flat surface of a reg of fine sand and dust, leaving pebbles and larger stones. No wonder a reg is sometimes called desert pavement. The rocks protect the underneath layers from further wind erosion.

Mirages, phantom rain, that appears to human eyes but does not exist, and other tricks of the desert have had endless fascination for men from all walks of life. Today's scientists are barely beginning to turn their attention to the deserts, in search of new sources of water to develop farmland and to recover more of its mineral wealth.

Desert Wealth: Petroleum

Here and there in the deserts one

A geologist examines a rock sample in the field

Oil pipelines carry crude oil across the desert of Libya

can understand how they lie and what structures they have. These are just some of the ways in which scientists begin the search for more "black gold" beneath the desert.

Today the search for deposits of other valuable chemicals is a new challenge. For example, the Spanish government, in partnership with an American firm, is beginning to mine phosphates for chemical fertilizers at a lonely spot in the Spanish Sahara. There, at Bu-Craa, the only visitors once were camel caravans and fierce desert nomads. Someday this lonely oasis may be the source of enough fertilizer to help feed almost seventy million people a year, for geologists have found one of the richest phosphate deposits in the world. Someday a conveyor belt may carry ore from the midst of seemingly endless dunes to the sea forty miles away for shipment to far parts of the world. This is one of many beginnings in recovering treasures from the desert.

So it is with the search for water beneath the desert's surface. Underground water is making it possible to farm in some parts of the Sahara on an experimental basis. That is another frontier where scientists have much to learn. It is another earth puzzle in which scientists are putting pieces together for the benefit of man.

finds efficient, air conditioned living quarters for geologists who are searching for oil and gas deposits trapped beneath the sands and layers of sandstone, shale, limestone, and other materials deep in the ground. Suppose a geologist is asked to locate oil in a vast expanse of desert. This is not an easy task, for the oil is trapped in small areas and there is little or no surface evidence of where it lies. After making a detailed survey of the area, the geologist can investigate further areas that seem interesting. Gravity meters are used to measure from point to point any variation in the gravitational pull caused by undulations deep in the crust of the earth. Such variations are very minute.

Other instruments may give hints, too. Magnetometers measure minute variations in magnetic forces under the earth. Sometimes such variations are due to structures that lead to deposits of oil or gas. Seismograph crews measure the time it takes for waves to travel through the earth after charges of dynamite set up tiny earthquakes in holes that are drilled by rigs. Since the waves bounce back from underground layers of rocks, geologists

The world has many types of desert and icy wastelands.

70

NORTH
AMERICA

SOUTH
AMERICA

AFRICA

ASIA

AUSTRALIA

CHAPTER VII

THE MYSTERY
OF MOUNTAINS

Suppose you could arrange to have your body frozen in such a way that you could be thawed at intervals of ten thousand years. Then you could look around, record what you saw, and produce a wonderful record for historians, including the scientists who are studying the history and the structure of the earth.

Perhaps you have never thought of geologists as historians. One of the difficulties in this science is the slow pace at which many processes take place, making the history of the earth dependent on clues from the far past. One example of a slow earth process is mountain building. Except for volcanoes, the hills seem everlasting and unchanging, but this is far from true.

Scientists can measure the height of a mountain and compare it with new measurements years later in order to see whether it has grown or diminished in size. But there are many problems involved. The height of Mount Everest has always been of special interest because it is the highest known mountain on the earth. More than a hundred years ago, British surveyors made measurements of the height of Mount Everest from six different places and averaged their figures. Strangely enough, the average came to exactly 29,000 feet. Since it seemed unlikely that the height of the mountain could be such an even number of feet, they added two feet for the official figure. Even though these men had measured very carefully, they were aware of the difficulties involved, and they knew that they could not really measure Mount Everest to the exact foot. About a hundred years later, a group of Indians surveyed the height and came up with a figure of 29,028 feet. Was this difference of twenty-six feet a mistake in accuracy of measurement, or had the mountain grown? No one really knows.

If you could check the height of a mountain every ten thousand years, the figures might show a much wider variation. Some places that are now mountainous might be just hilly. Some places that are now flat might have rugged mountains. One of the things that geologists do not question is the rising and wearing down of mountains. This they know is very true, and they have much evidence for it.

Glaciers are a major instrument in the wearing down of mountains. The famous peak of the Matterhorn is a good example of glacial erosion. As mentioned in the last chapter, the ice of a glacier carries

Mountains cover large areas of the earth's surface

tons of rocks with it. One can even see great piles of rocks at the mouth of a glacier. This glacial moraine, as it is called, is often visible in places around the earth where glaciers have long since melted.

Glacial moraines are made of all the material that is blown on a glacier and that falls on it, and from material that is picked up from the valley beneath as the glacier moves along. It ranges in size from bits of dust to rocks that weigh thousands of tons. Sometimes the amount of material in the moraine is so great that it covers the surface of the ice. The work of glaciers in moving large quantities of rock from mountain tops to valley floors is tremendous.

Millions of tons of snow sometimes scour the side of a mountain in the form of an avalanche. The "white death" is a constant threat to those who live in some parts of the world, especially Switzerland. Avalanches can be triggered by natural causes, for the snow may begin to slide under its own weight after a heavy snowstorm. Even snow falling from trees can begin a snowslide. Or the vibrations caused by a car driving past a bank of snow, the slamming of a door, or the pressure of a pair of skis can trigger an avalanche.

Scientists are studying ways to protect people by building better defenses against avalanches and by learning more about the exact spots where they may occur. Perhaps you have heard the explosions caused by dynamite early in the mornings at ski resorts, where men are setting avalanches in motion before opening the trails to skiers. No matter what the cause, when an avalanche rushes down a mountainside, it takes along everything in its path.

Scientists and engineers are learning to protect man and his buildings from landslides, another factor in

A mountain range in Bavaria.

74

the wearing away of hills and mountains. The new Puget Sound Power and Light Company plant, in the state of Washington, is an example of this. Several years ago, hundreds of tons of earth from the bank of a nearby river crashed onto the old building and destroyed it. The new building's sloped roof of reinforced concrete should permit any sliding earth to pass right over it without damage.

The Work of Running Water

The work of running water in wearing down mountains is not as dramatic as that of landslides, but it plays a larger part because of the vast amount that flows. The countless little threads that trickle downhill and the mighty rivers that rage or flow peacefully along the countryside all carry a certain amount of sediment. Tons upon tons of soil, rock, and other debris of assorted sizes are carried along from a variety of slopes ranging from flatlands to rugged mountainsides.

Picture some barren soil in an almost flat field. Hard rain carries a load of soil to a nearby ditch. Perhaps some of the soil stays there for years before more rains carry it to a mud bar or a small stream. Sooner or later, the soil will travel some route to a river that empties into a lake or sea. So it is with dirt,

Climbers stand near the summit of the Matterhorn; glaciers have given this famous mountain its rugged shape

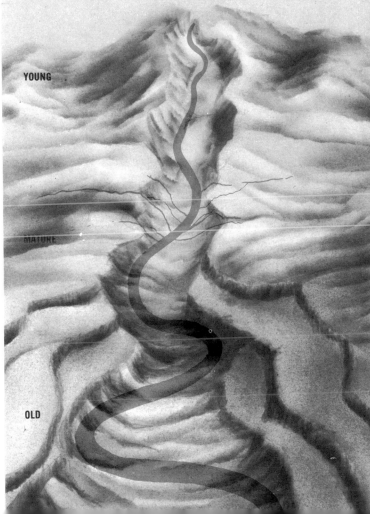

Rivers go through erosion cycles which geologists term "young," "mature," and "old"; notice different types of rivers in each landscape

YOUNG

MATURE

OLD

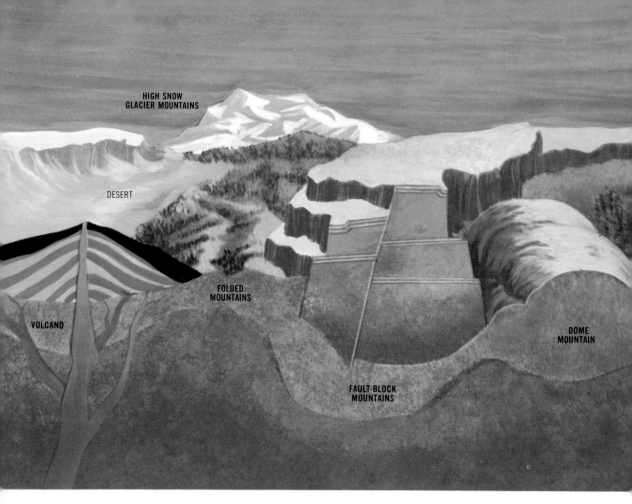

HIGH SNOW
GLACIER MOUNTAINS

DESERT

FOLDED
MOUNTAINS

VOLCANO

DOME
MOUNTAIN

FAULT-BLOCK
MOUNTAINS

The landscape of the earth has developed in many different ways; a cross-section exposes several land forms

The famous Painted Desert in Arizona

rocks, and so forth from slopes, from hills, from mountains. They are slowly and constantly wearing down, and the worn parts make a long journey to become sediment at some other place.

Wind and the particles it carries, changes in weather, and many other forces of erosion help wear down the mountains. Usually the process is very, very slow, taking hundreds or even thousands of years to build up a layer of soil a foot thick at the mouth of a river in the sea. If new mountains were not being built, eventually the old ones would be worn away, leaving a flat earth.

Mountain Building

Mountain building is more exciting than the wearing down of

mountains. It is also more mysterious, for it is still not fully understood even by the men and women who devote much of their lives to studying the problem. There are many theories, but none completely explains the origin of mountains.

Have you heard the story that the mountains of the earth were formed when the earth cooled and shrank? Mountains were the wrinkles in the earth's crust, much like the wrinkles in the skin of an old apple that has dried and shrunk. About fifty years ago, Clarence Dutton, a famous American geologist, showed that this could not be true, for the patterns of folding that could be found in the rocks of mountains were not the same as those that would result from the crust of a shrinking earth. Today most scientists debate the shrinking of a hot, new earth and favor the idea of a cool origin. So there is added reason to search for new explanations of the causes of mountain building.

Scientists believe that mountains form in a number of different ways. Knowing something about the inside of the earth helps us understand the upward thrust. Since no one is really certain about what is far beneath our feet, it is no wonder that no one is certain exactly how mountains are built.

It has been suggested that one think of the earth as a pillow that, if punched in one spot, bulges out in others. If the earth is pliable in the region of Moho, shifting of weight caused by the wearing down of mountains can be easily seen as a force in mountain building.

As sediment is deposited, no matter how slow the rate, there is added pressure on the part beneath. The weight of sediments can cause depressions in the land. This can force the deposits into narrower areas so that they are compressed, and such compressions can produce the folding and faulting of rocks. When the stress in the earth, caused by the pressure of sediments, is relieved by folding and faulting, some of the rocks can be lifted up to become mountain ridges. This theory was advanced by an American geologist, James Hall, long ago, but it is a part of the story of the earth that has not been entirely rewritten. His theory is still accepted as one explanation of mountain building, although there is more involved, and his theory of geosyncline (or "earth bending together") has been modified. Today's geologists believe that there are vertical forces at work as well as the squeezing-together from the sides, as shown on page 78.

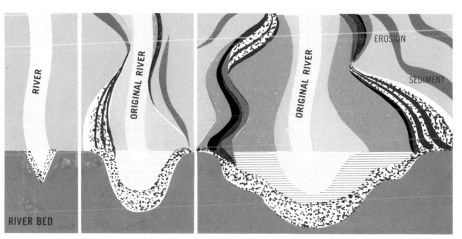

Rivers widen as they grow older

RIVER

ORIGINAL RIVER

ORIGINAL RIVER

EROSION

SEDIMENT

RIVER BED

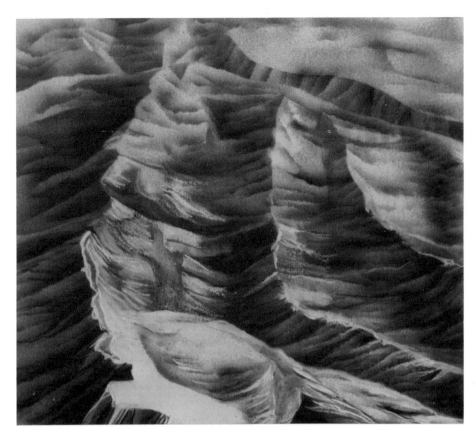

Huge folds of rock formed the Rocky Mountains, giving the range its shape

There are many questions about geosynclines that are still unanswered, but geologists believe that the principal mountain chains in the world have a similar history, based on the geosynclines, for they are composed mainly of folded sedimentary rocks.

The Rocky Mountains of the United States, which were formed about eighty million years ago, are a relatively young chain of folded mountains. Like most mountains, their history is long and complex. The following is a very simplified description of their life story.

The Rocky Mountains probably began with the formation of a geosyncline. First, there was a vast trough in the earth's crust that was a few hundred miles wide and almost 2,000 miles in length. This trough existed long before the cowboy days, long before the days of the Indians, long before any men lived on earth. Water in the trough made a large inland sea that divided the continent into two land masses, but sediment filled it almost as fast as the bottom of it sank, and the sea remained rather shallow. Gradually, the fill formed layered sedimentary rock. This whole process took about one hundred million years.

The next stage in the history of the Rocky Mountains is a dramatic one. The floor of the geosyncline described above buckled into folds, some of which were great arches. Rocks were folded and fractured. On the eastern side, the part that is now Colorado and Wyoming, the granite floor was lifted far above sea

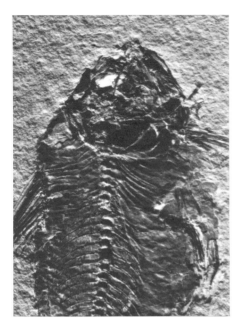

Skeletons and shells of ancient fish and shellfish have been found high in the Rocky Mountains, proving that these rocks were at one time under the ocean

A geologist collects a fossil for study

level, and sedimentary rock made high mountains that from a distance look like high walls. On the western side, large folds were overturned toward the east. They were broken by huge faults, and a tremendous mountain complex was formed by the piling of great slices of sedimentary rock thousands of feet each, one on top of the other. Geologists estimate that this phase lasted for about ten to fifteen million years.

The next stage consisted of slow wearing down by erosion, with the gradual filling of some of the basins. And then there was another stage of gentle uplift by further erosion in a complicated pattern, which led to the condition one sees there today. Eventually, the Rocky Mountains will wear away, but if one visits them today, that is hard to believe.

The Rocky Mountains are caused mainly by the folding of rocks that have buckled and fractured. One of the many interesting things about folded mountains is the frequent presence of marine fossils high above the level of the sea. This gives evidence that some of the highest peaks arose from the floors of ancient seas.

Cross-section of a typical fault

The San Andreas Fault in California extends in an almost straight line for miles

Found with the folding, and sometimes found in cases where there is no folding of rocks, large faults or breaks can play a major part in the building of mountains. Faults and the part they play in earthquakes were mentioned earlier in this book. It is not surprising that earthquakes and mountain building sometimes go hand in hand, since the forces of uplift also begin deep within the earth.

When faulting occurs again and again in the same place over a long period of time, entire mountains may be reared by this kind of vertical shifting. Mountains that are built this way are called fault-block mountains. One example is the Sierra Nevada of California, a single tilted block that is sixty miles wide and four hundred miles long.

There are scientists who believe that some mountain formation may be due to the pulling on the earth from the moon. The moon pulls on the waters of the earth as it

Astronauts study geologic formations near Meteor Crater in Arizona

passes around the earth in its orbit, thus creating tides. Scientists who study the earth know that the moon's gravitational pull affects the land part of the earth's surface, too. As the moon passes over it, the crust of the earth swells outward, creating tension on the rocky crust. Might it be true that some hills and valleys in the earth's crust form and deepen because of the moon? Many scientists challenge this theory of mountain building, but more studies are being made to measure the motion in the earth's crust due to tidal effect. Equipment has been installed in a mine in New Jersey by Columbia University's Lamont Geological Observatory to help obtain a more complete picture of the contraction and expansion of the earth's crust. It is agreed that the moon plays a major role in causing the solid part of the earth to rise and fall about six inches in a twelve-hour period. Just how much a part this plays through the years in the slow process of mountain building is still a mystery.

Certainly, there is much to be learned about mountain building. The most common types of mountain formation are folding and faulting, but the mountains built by volcanoes are perhaps the most awe-inspiring of all. Because they are so dramatic, and because they form a "chain of fire" around the earth, many books have been written about those forces that help to shape the land and the bottom of the seas. Just a few of the stories of volcanoes are told in the next chapter.

CHAPTER VIII

THE STORY
OF VOLCANOES

The story of volcanoes is as old as time and as new as tomorrow. While scientists explore what may have been the famous lost island of Atlantis, astronauts are flying to Iceland to study lava flows and volcanoes so that they will be better prepared to study what they will find when they land on the surface of the moon. Today's story of volcanoes is one of action, ranging from knowledge gained by studying the strange events of the past to the discovery of volcanoes on other planets.

First, look at the forces in the earth that scientists believe cause the dramatic birth of an island or the sudden explosions from long-extinct volcanoes. Although volcanoes vary widely in size and shape and in the kind of material they eject, they all involve the activities of magma, and each has its own "personality." Magma is molten material from beneath the surface of the earth. Most volcanoes produce lava, for lava is magma that has reached the surface of the earth through cracks and fissures. It consists of very hot rock, so hot that the rock is liquid, along with steam from hot water and other gases. Magma comes originally from the earth's crust or from the upper mantle and works its way to the surface. Although much is known about magma, it is not fully understood.

Inside a Volcano

What happens deep inside a volcano? Toward the bottom of the earth's crust, hot rock maintains its solid state because of the pressure from rock above it. When pressure is reduced by a crack in the earth or rock that lies above, the hot rock can change to a liquid in a small chamber known as a magma chamber. Zones of weakness, regions of lessened pressure, or already existing fissures are perfect paths for the passage of magma. Gas pressure in pockets in the earth forces the magma to move. Sometimes as magma moves, it melts overlying rocks or forces them aside.

Magma may be between one thousand and two thousand degrees Fahrenheit when it starts to flow, but eventually it cools and becomes solid rock, one of the types of igneous rock mentioned earlier. It may cool enough to solidify before it reaches the surface of the earth, or it may cool after it rolls down the side of a volcano. Some magma is hurled high in the air, carrying solid rocks with it, in violent eruption. Such an eruption is

Molten lava flows down the slopes of Kilauea in Hawaii

An undersea volcano off Iceland throws steam and smoke skyward during an eruption one of the most spectacular sights on earth. Whether a volcano emits magma that wells up slowly from time to time and flows far out to build a broad cone, or whether it erupts intermittently and violently, a volcano is a natural laboratory for scientists who study the earth. In many cases, observation stations are maintained near the summits of volcanoes, even during times when the volcanoes are active.

Volcanoes may remain dormant for thousands of years and then suddenly burst into violence when the pressure has built up beneath the ground. Such eruptions have caused many deaths; the famous eruption of Vesuvius in 79 A.D. completely buried the cities of Pompeii and Herculaneum. Vil-lages had grown up around the base of Vesuvius, and its fertile slopes were covered with vineyards. Poison gases, falling cinders, and ash overwhelmed the people of the two cities so quickly that an estimated 1,600 people had no time to flee. The remains of their buildings are visited by many tourists each year. Some of the more adventurous climb the slope of Vesuvius and peer into its crater. Although there have been lesser eruptions since 79 A.D., Vesuvius is usually quiet.

One particularly interesting, but horrible, disaster caused by a violent volcanic eruption is the one that occurred on Martinique in 1902. Martinique is a lovely island in the warm Caribbean Ocean; the city of St. Pierre is located about six

The eruption of Mount Pelée destroyed the city of St. Pierre in Martinique

miles from Mount Pelée, a small volcanic mountain. The vegetation is lush and the tropical flowers beautiful; but on that famous day in May the volcano burst apart and destroyed all but two of the city's 30,000 inhabitants within three minutes.

suddenly dark. He felt his arms and legs burning as he entered his house. A number of others who sought refuge there died in great pain from the heat, even though their clothes had not caught fire. For some unknown reason, the shoemaker was the only one in the

Building destroyed in the eruption of Mount Pelée

Perhaps you are wondering how lava from a volcano six miles away could have accomplished such destruction in so short a time. Actually, the people were scorched to death by a glowing cloud of hot gases and incandescent particles in which there was not enough oxygen to support burning or breathing. After the cloud passed, a supply of oxygen returned, and the city was soon aflame. The heat was so great even before the fire that many objects, such as pages in books, turned to charcoal, and some food-stuffs resembled petrified materials. Glass in some of the bottles became soft, and the bottles sagged out of shape.

One of the survivors was a shoe-maker who lived on the fringe area affected by the glowing cloud. He described the beginning of the disaster as a sudden and terrible wind, a trembling earth, and a sky

house who survived. He managed to run away in spite of bleeding legs that were covered with burns.

The other survivor was a prisoner who was jailed in a dungeon that was poorly ventilated. He had no barred window, just a tiny grating at the door. While the prisoner was awaiting his breakfast in his cell, there was a sudden darkness. A hot blast of air rushed through the grating. The prisoner, who had no idea what was happening, screamed for help, but no one was left in the city to help him. Even though his clothing did not catch fire, he was severely burned. According to reports, he lived four long days without food or water or attention to his burns before he was rescued by sightseers from a nearby village. He was pardoned for his crime and spent the rest of his life touring in a circus as the "Prisoner of Saint Pierre."

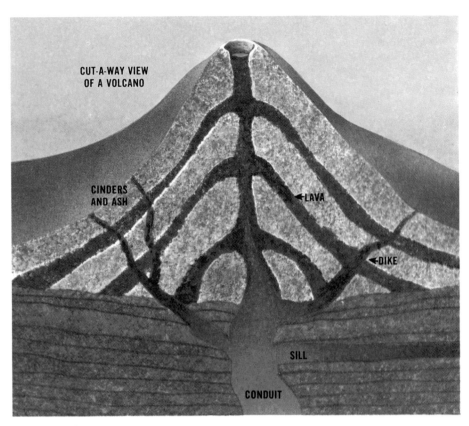

CUT-A-WAY VIEW
OF A VOLCANO

CINDERS
AND ASH

◄LAVA

◄DIKE

SILL

CONDUIT

An exposed view of a volcano

There are many stories of disaster from the eruption of volcanoes, even though most volcanoes are extinct. There may be as many as five hundred active vents, but there are thousands of dormant volcanoes. Dormant volcanoes could become active, but extinct ones are not expected to erupt again.

Rings of Fire

"Rings of fire," or chains of volcanoes, are always associated with places where the crust of the earth is actively changing. There is one chain around the Pacific Ocean; another group exists in the area of the Mediterranean. Still another chain of volcanoes lies in the Rift Valley in eastern Africa. Volcanoes that were active long ago played a part in the formation of the Alps, but they are no longer part of a chain of fire. As with other forces on and in the earth, there is an ever-changing pattern.

One of the most spectacular volcanic eruptions is often called the "shot heard round the world." In 1883 the island of Krakatoa in the Java Sea was the scene of a series of volcanic explosions that scattered ash over the entire earth and caused sound vibrations that could be heard 3,000 miles away. This explosion was one of the greatest in history, much greater than a large number of hydrogen bombs exploding at one time. Half the volcano was blown away, and about 36,000 people died in the wake of the giant ocean waves it sent out through the seas. Krakatoa has long been famous as the island that blew its top.

In 1967 the puzzle of the location of a famous volcano may have been answered. Since the time of Plato, men have been searching for the

An artist's conception of the lost continent of Atlantis

beneath the vineyards on the island of Thera. It contains two- and three-story houses intact. A whole town—with frescoes beautifully preserved, jugs still filled with olive oil and wine, skeletons of dogs, pigs, and other animals—has all been well preserved. Since valuable treasures such as gold and jewelry are lacking, it is believed that the volcano gave some warning before it erupted. The people must have had time to flee before its ashes covered the city, for human skeletons are also lacking.

Some day, you may visit that city, which may have been Atlantis. You will go underground through a tunnel to reach the remains. There, a huge volcano exploded with a force five times greater than that of the famous Krakatoa. There, a volcano preserved history for thousands of years.

Birth of a Volcano

Paracutin is a volcano with a very different story. It is famous as the only one whose complete life cycle was watched by scientists. Most existing volcanoes are very, very old. But Paracutin began and

The Hiklo volcano erupts on Iceland

so-called lost continent of Atlantis. They believed it was on the bottom of the Atlantic Ocean, where it sunk following a volcanic eruption. Oceanographers, after making careful soundings, agreed with those who believed that the story of Atlantis was a myth.

A peasant's donkey may have led scientists to the real location of Atlantis, which was not beneath the Atlantic Ocean but in the Mediterranean Sea, under Thera.

Thera is an island in the Sea of Crete where a volcano exploded and blanketed cities with volcanic ash and pumice about 3,500 years ago. There, a peasant's donkey stepped on the floor of a cave hollowed out of the cliffs. The floor collapsed. And this led men to one of the most exciting finds of all time.

Today, geologists, archeologists, and other scientists are studying a prehistoric town that was found

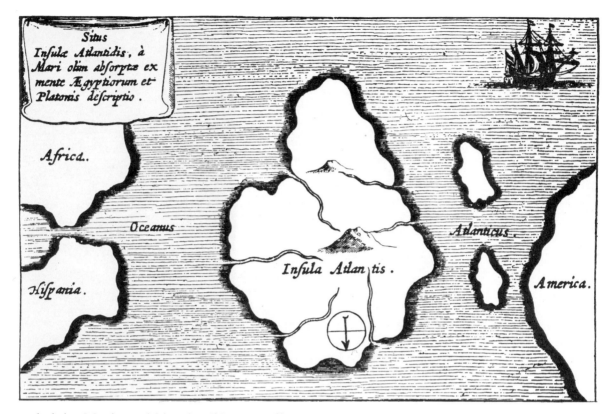

An ancient map of Atlantis;
such maps were, of course,
drawn from imagination

ended in Mexico within the life-
times of most people who are alive
today. A farmer who noticed a
cloud of smoke rising from the
ground while he was plowing his
cornfield never could have guessed
that it would become the site of a
volcano with so much fiery lava
bursting from its flanks that it eventually engulfed the village of San
Juan Parangaricutiro about six
miles away. The volcano grew
slowly for a year, and the cone grew
to a height of a thousand feet. It
was a beautiful and awesome sight.
After nine years the activity died,
and there has been little or no action since then.

Each volcano has its own indi-
vidual life history, for each volcano
is different from every other one.
But each is just part of the natural
process of mountain building
brought about by disturbances deep
within the earth. The volcano Paracutin was born after several days of

small earthquakes, including one
day on which as many as two hundred were recorded. In spite of
rumblings under the earth farmers
and villagers did not suspect the
birth of a new volcano, but scientists
have had some success in predicting
when dormant volcanoes will begin
again to gush smoke, steam, and
fiery liquid rock.

In one study of volcanoes, scientists of the U.S. Geological Survey
drilled into the Hawaiian volcano
known as Kilauea Iki, which had
erupted about eight years before
their experiment. A considerable
amount of lava had been trapped
in the crater and formed a quiet
lake of molten rock. The lake
crusted over as the top of it cooled,
forming a black crust about eighty-
seven feet thick. By drilling beneath the crust, geologists brought
some of the still molten basalt rock
to the surface and took its temperature. They found it to be 2,000

degrees Fahrenheit. Compare this with the temperature of boiling water at 212 degrees Fahrenheit. They can continue studies beneath the surface by using the drill hole they made to learn more about the development of minerals as lava cools and more about the changes in temperature and the composition of volcanic gases.

New volcanoes are always especially interesting to scientists. The world's newest island, Surtsey, is such a treasure of scientific information about the earth that it has been declared a national preserve, so that it can be studied before tourists contaminate it. Surtsey was born in 1963 in the North Atlantic Ocean about seventy-five miles southeast of Reykjavik, Iceland, and twenty miles off the Icelandic coast. Iceland is the largest above-sea section of the long Mid-Atlantic Ridge that reaches from the South Atlantic to north of the Arctic Circle. A zone of volcanic activity cuts across Iceland, but no one was expecting the birth of an island from beneath the sea when fishermen first reported dark smoke rising above the water. From the floor of the ocean, lava pushed up and piled up until it reached the surface. Fishermen reported a boat on fire when they sent an SOS to the nearest Coast Guard station, but no boat was in the area. Three hours after the first report, the column of erupting gases and rock had risen to a height of 1,200 feet or perhaps as much as 1,500 feet.

Imagine the thrill of watching a new island being born in the ocean! Scientists flying above reported that ash, cinders, and pumice rushed up in a heavy, black cloud. They estimated that the volcano's steam would surpass by 100,000 times the energy produced by Niagara Falls if it could have been

This huge fire pit in the Kilauean crater contains pools of molten lava

harnessed in the early violent stages. In four years, the island grew to a 670-acre pile of lava, ash, and rock. By then, its activity was irregular, but sometimes it sent out smoke, steam, and fiery rocks that glowed in the night.

Surtsey is one of the first volcanic islands that has had its temperature taken from outer space. On August 20, 1967, the U.S. National Aeronautics and Space Administration's

Nimbus 2 weather satellite passed over Surtsey and took measurements that were returned to earth and examined by geologists who were working on various aspects of volcanoes. Such measurements may be helpful in using satellites to detect volcanoes on Mars and other bodies in space. The Earth Resources Observation Satellite program continues to examine volcanoes from high in the sky to obtain knowledge that adds to man's understanding of the weather and the earth beneath him. The study from space may provide some clues to more accurate prediction of volcanic activity.

Whole chains of islands are sometimes built in the ocean by volcanoes that erupt time and time again. That is how the Hawaiian Islands and the Aleutian Islands were created. Tremendous amounts of material have arisen from deep in the earth in this island-building process. The Hawaiian volcanoes are the world's highest

Steam from volcanic action comes from long cracks in the ground

mountains if one measures from their bases in the sea to their summits.

The Process of Volcano Making

Engineers use light beams to measure distances across volcanic craters; such beams can detect small variations in distances

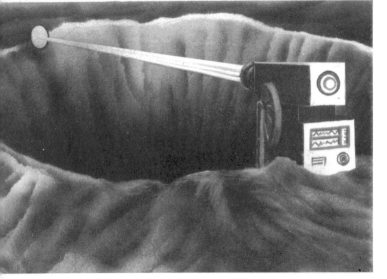

The process of volcano making is being studied constantly by scientists on the slopes of many volcanoes. They record minute earth tremors and the slight increase in the tilt of the land around the craters that often precedes activity in old volcanoes, so that they can learn more about prediction of flows that may harm people living nearby.

A new geological tool, a beam of light waves or radio waves, is being put to work to help learn more that will help predict volcanic eruptions. Such electronic beams were used during an eruption at Kilauea volcano in Hawaii. Generally, as molten rock moves up a volcano's vent, the sides of the crater are tilted outward because the volcano expands. When the lava pours down the sides of the volcano, or when it flows back down the vent, the sides contract. If a transmitter is set at the edge of a volcano, it can send a light or radio beam across the crater. When the beam hits a reflector at the opposite side, it bounces back. When there is a slight change in the diameter of the crater, either because of expansion or contraction, the outgoing and incoming pulses of the electronic beam are altered. Scientists say they are out of phase. Such a change may be a warning signal that can help geologists anticipate an

Views of Pompeii, Italy, a city destroyed by Vesuvius

explosive eruption and warn surrounding inhabitants if they feel that danger is imminent.

Dr. Alexander McBirney, director of the Center for Volcanology at the University of Oregon in the United States, believes that many eruptions could be predicted and much destruction prevented if governments of the world would provide money for a constant watch on potentially dangerous volcanoes. Underground activity cannot be heard by residents of an area, but it can be detected by geologists' instruments in advance of an explosion. Warning signals that precede volcanic activity include shock waves in the area, changes in magnetic field, and variations in the level of the ground. There are a growing number of volcanological stations in various parts of the world. These stations and volcano research are helping to make prediction more accurate.

The effects of volcanic activity are not all bad. One reason that the tragedy caused by volcanoes is so easily forgotten from generation to generation is the rich soil that de-velops slowly after the flow of lava down a mountainside. The ejected material that comes from inside the volcano is unbelievably fertile. After the volcano cools and the material becomes workable as soil, farmers flock to the slopes, where they can sometimes produce several good crops a year. With such soil fertility, the hazard is soon forgotten.

Perhaps the most important product of volcanic activity is geothermal heat, a source of power that is barely beginning to be developed. Although men have long used waters heated by the cooling of shallowly covered bodies of magma at health spas, putting steam from within the earth to work to produce electricity is relatively new and rare. Perhaps some day man will prospect for steam somewhat the way he does for oil and gas, to help turn the wheels of the world. No matter when man begins to tap the heat of the earth for power, it will always be there. Volcanoes are about as old as the earth, and they will continue their rumbling for years and years to come.

CHAPTER IX

EARTH AT
THE EDGE
OF THE SEA

Someday you may open a vacation map that shows places to visit on the earth beneath the sea. Here and there along the coasts, tourists are already being invited to explore underwater parks. They don snorkel and flippers and follow a guide through crystal-clear water to look at the floor of the sea's edge. Corals, grottoes, and canyons are marked with waterproof signs. They are unusual and fascinating vacation parks.

Explorers of the edge of the sea are searching there for new living quarters for the men of tomorrow, for it is not impossible that the threatening population explosion will push some dwellers underwater. More immediately than living space, the earth at the edge of the sea promises to become a treasure chest of wealth in minerals, including diamonds and other resources. Scientists have predicted that many of tomorrow's raw materials will come from the water of the oceans and the land beneath them.

The wonders of the sea have challenged men from the time of earliest man until the present day. Tomorrow the sea will have more meaning for a greater number of people. New technology is already helping men to explore its depths and unravel some of the secrets hidden there. Only about fifteen years ago men believed that the mysteries of the deep would always remain mysteries, that man would never get to the dark floor of the ocean, which lies crushed beneath the pressure of seven tons of water per square inch above it. Certainly, the science of the sea is young, and its future is great. Think of the exciting discoveries that may lie ahead!

Man has long enjoyed the vast beauty of the oceans; but those who live along the coasts have learned to fight their fury. It has often been said that the sea draws the map, for waves and sand deposits mean the birth and death of harbors. As the wind and the sea shape the edge of the land, men fight to retain the lines that they want. They resort to methods centuries old, such as rock piles for jetties, and they try new ideas, such as plastic bags full of sand, in their efforts to hold back the sea. Sometimes they are successful. Sometimes the sea comes in, carrying beaches and large numbers of houses back with it.

One especially interesting study of the earth along the edge of the sea is the tagging of sand with radioactivity. Sand is sent from distant beaches to scientists of the

U.S. Atomic Energy Commission at Oak Ridge, Tennessee, where a special process is used to irradiate the sand. Such sand will cause a click in an instrument known as a Geiger counter when it is close to the counter, and the sand is thus tagged so that it can be easily recognized. The sand is then shipped from Tennessee to its original place on the beach. Perhaps you are wondering why sand from a distant beach rather than local sand must be tagged. Scientists have found that sand behaves differently away from its original beach, so much transportation is necessary to make the study accurate. After sand has been tagged, scientists can track its paths to learn more about the movements at the surface of the earth where land and sea meet.

From the watery edge of the sandy beaches and the rocks along the coast to the continental slopes that skirt the continents, the waters teem with life. More and more, man looks to the coastal waters to help feed a crowded world. The continental shelves, too, hold great promise for the very near future. If man could work and live freely there, he would add an area as large as the continent of Africa to the usable part of the earth.

Continental Shelves

If all the water could be drained from the edge of the sea, one would see the vast shelves that slope gently away from the coast until the water reaches a depth of five to six hundred feet. In some places the shelves are absent, while in others they are often as wide as a hundred miles, and there is one 800 miles wide. They skirt the shores of North America and link Borneo, Java, Sumatra, and the Philippines to the mainland. The British Isles are surrounded by the European continental shelf.

In general, the surface of the continental shelf is fairly flat. In many places the shelf drops so gently that you would not notice enough incline to guide you toward the coast or away from it. A diver

A cross-section showing the continental shelf and the earth's crust under the ocean

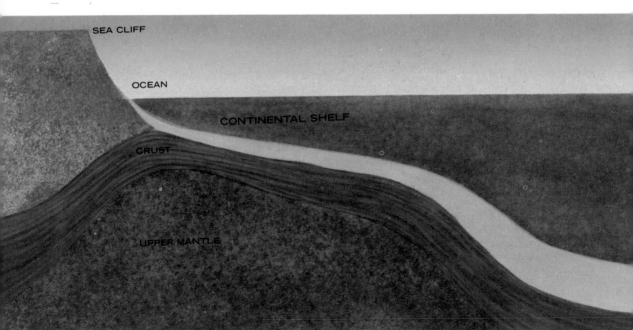

SEA CLIFF

OCEAN

CONTINENTAL SHELF

CRUST

UPPER MANTLE

CONTINENTAL
SHELF

SEDIMENT
BUILD UP

lost underwater might wish for more of a slope.

At the outer edge of the continental shelves, the earth drops more suddenly. There is a natural boundary or wall, known as the continental slope, that divides the shelf from the deep ocean. The angle of the slope varies greatly, from very gentle to very steep. Where mountains meet the sea, the drop may be a tremendously long one from peak to canyon. At one place in South America the earth drops from the highest peak in the Andes to the bottom of the Peru-Chile trench for a distance of nine miles. Five miles of the drop is below the surface of the sea. Can you imagine a slope that drops nine miles through a horizontal distance of a hundred? This is probably the greatest slope in the world. What a view it would make, if one could see it all, rather than just the part above the surface of the water!

The surface of the continental slope has some spectacular gorges in it. Scientists who probe its surface sometimes find canyons that were once thought to be drowned river beds. Today, oceanographers and other earth scientists believe that these gorges in the slopes may have been cut by powerful avalanches that occur undersea when torrents of silt-laden water rush down the slopes. Such water is more dense than regular sea water, and an avalanche might take place much as it would on land when there is an imbalance. Silt-laden currents, called turbidity currents, can gouge out a canyon and spread thick layers of sediment over an area of hundreds of miles. This motion goes on beneath the surface of the sea unnoticed by peoples around the world. Watching such an avalanche would be exciting, but living near one would indeed be dangerous.

Maps of the continental shelf and slope are shedding new light on the

The bottom of the ocean, if dry, would look like this

The continental shelves of the United States

97

earth at the edge of the sea. Vacation maps of this area may be a long time in coming, but detailed maps of some areas are already for sale from the United States Government Printing Office in Washington, D.C. They are technical documents of marine geology, the most detailed of their kind ever published. Such maps include the thickness of the sediment, the geological nature of the bedrock, and the intensity of the earth's magnetic field at various places. This information may be of little interest to those who sail their boats on the surface water, but for those who might search for gold, diamonds, oil, and other treasures in the earth under the water, they are important. Certain fish congregate and feed near rock formations, so fishermen too will be helped by detailed topographic maps. So will engineers who build undersea pipelines, cables, and platforms for oil rigs on the continental shelf.

In other parts of the world oceanographers are exploring their local continental shelves for similar reasons.

Ocean-Going Laboratories

Many ocean-going laboratories have gathered data for maps of the continental shelves over a period of many years. Some of today's ships are electronically equipped with an assortment of instruments that measure the temperature, depth, and salinity of the sea and other data and report them to a computer at the heart of the system. This is a vastly improved method of learning about the earth beneath the sea compared with the old methods of taking soundings, gathering quantities of data, and having them processed in an office back on land over a period of months. On the newest ocean research ships a computer aboard ship receives information that is fed to it by tape and processes it, making it available for transmission to ships in other areas as well as to shore stations.

Instruments aboard research ships not only probe the depth of the ocean and the shape of the floor of the sea but also investigate the material under the surface of the floor to get a profile of the subbottom. If man is to mine the material on the ocean floor and beneath it, he needs detailed maps of large areas of the surface of the continental shelf and the material of which it is made.

In addition to enlarged programs of exploration by new manned research ships, a program is underway to develop unmanned launches that can operate in fleets, sounding the sea floor and telemetering information back to a mother ship. Instead of sending three or four launches from a mother ship, with a crew of four or more on each launch, drones can operate in fleets of ten or twenty using an automatic pilot that responds to a mother ship's command unit.

Another method of learning more about the earth beneath the edge of the sea is by setting off explosions along the sea bottom. Buoys in which there are hydrophones that

Many divers wear diving clothes and have scuba equipment

Scientists wait for a ship in the Antarctic

record seismic waves on magnetic tape are anchored in the test area. The seismic waves set up by the explosions are timed so that they are accurate to within one-hundredth of a second. They provide information about the kind of material through which the waves travel, so that men can learn more about the material that lies between the coast and the outer edge of the continental shelf.

These are just a few of the projects some explorers are using to increase their knowledge by studying the bottom of the edge of the sea from its surface. Others are exploring the bottom first-hand. One series of experiments in living underwater, called Sealab, is attempting to extend man's ability to explore and exploit the ocean floor to the limits of the world's continental shelves. Under the direction of the United States Navy, many experiments have been performed inside and outside the capsules.

Tuffy, a trained bottle-nosed dolphin, was part of an experiment in using animals to deliver messages and to help divers in distress. One Sealab capsule was nicknamed "Tiltin' Hilton" because it was on the edge of a deep sea canyon and the floor beneath it was not level. The deck of the capsule was at an angle, so plates had to be held so that they would not slide across the table when the men were eating. Pots and pans had to be tied to the stove so that they would not slide off. These were just a few of the

minor problems of living in this underwater home. Cramped quarters where every inch serves a purpose, breathable atmosphere in an underwatercraft, diseases resulting from the strange conditions, psychological problems, and dangers from marine life are just a few of the problems with which those who search underwater must cope. Even something as simple as emptying the trash and garbage can be a problem. In Sealab II, men cut the bottoms from cans and flattened them to make them smaller; but the garbage was a more unpleasant problem. Sometimes garbage was floated to the surface, where it could be picked up by surface workers. But when the pressure of the surrounding water burst the plastic bags of garbage as they rose, loose garbage rained back on the aquanauts.

Aquanauts at work in Sealab II

99

Sealab III aquanauts preparing for a dive

Aquanauts swimming near Sealab III deep in the ocean

To many men the seas are as great a challenge as outer space is. Commander Scott M. Carpenter, the second American astronaut to orbit the earth, left the space program in 1967 to continue deep-sea research in additional Sealab projects with the United States Navy.

Deep-Sea Research Vessels

Around the world, men are approaching the exploration of the earth's last frontier in a wide variety of ways. There are growing numbers of deep-sea research vessels being developed and tried in an effort to make use of the resources of the continental shelf and the water above it. One of these undersea research vessels is the *Seapup VI*, which can land on skis, hover, rotate, and maneuver in other ways without disturbing the floor of the ocean. *Deep Diver* is the name of a little yellow submarine that can put divers to work on the sea floor. It is a twenty-two-foot underwater taxi that travels to and from work areas aboard a mother vessel. Such a craft is a breakthrough for undersea construction and repairs. DOWB is the nickname of an ocean-work ship designed to do biological, acoustical, and physical work on the floor of the shelf. It can take its two-man crew to a depth of 6,500 feet. *Beaver Mark IV* carries three men and is built to extend mechanical arms that can lift fairly heavy weights. Another craft, the GSV-1, is designed to sit on the ocean floor at a depth of up to 2,000 feet and to act as an underwater home for a crew of six aquanauts. Still another, *Deep Quest,* is being built in such a way that it will give a diver support when he is as far as 1,000 feet from his underwater station, and it will be able to bore cores from the ocean floor to a depth of eight feet.

The exploration of the continental shelf by underwater research vessels and other methods has already brought to light some exciting information. For example, geologists have recently learned that small fossil shells in the bottom of the sea along the Atlantic coast indicate that the climate along the entire United States coast was as warm as the southern part is today. The fossils of warm-water dwellers that have been found are fifteen or more million years old. Such a climate change is of great interest to those who study the history of the earth.

Another recent discovery also concerns the earth long ago. About two million years ago there were probably wide beaches of sand for a mile or perhaps much more along the Atlantic coast between New Jersey and Florida. What a paradise for bathers if people had lived at that time to enjoy them.

Of more interest to the men who search for treasure beneath the coastal waters are discoveries (off the coast of Massachusetts) of pebbles composed of bauxite, an ore of aluminum. Since these pebbles were probably carried to their present location by a glacier, undiscovered bauxite deposits may exist

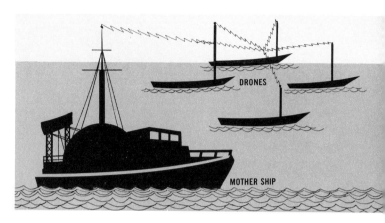

A mother ship directs drone ships

The Westinghouse Deepstar cruises along the bottom of the ocean

A new man-carrying diving chamber, the Chachalot, is raised after a trip to a depth of 600 feet

tion. Sophisticated techniques are needed to lower and install equipment, and even after an installation is made, mining must be controlled by remoted devices.

Mining on the floor of the shelves would obviously be much easier if men lived there in underwater cities.

Some of the most exciting work in the world of underwater living has been carried out under the direction of a French scientist, Captain Jacques-Yves Cousteau. His experiments, says Captain Cousteau, may be the forerunner of far larger underwater stations that will be manned in the future by scientists, miners, fish farmers, oil prospectors, and military personnel. Conshelf workshops, named for the continental shelf, have certainly pioneered man's economic occupation of the floor of the sea. Underwater camps have been the homes of many men working in the water

in the northern part of the Atlantic coastal plain.

Wresting the minerals from the continental shelf is a greater problem than discovering their loca-

A sonar search vehicle is lowered into the water; it can map the ocean floor to depths of 20,000 feet

for periods of weeks at a time. In one underwater building, a dome-topped yellow structure, there is a mess hall, a social center, and spokes that house bunks and equipment rooms. The starfish-type building is sometimes anchored with chains so that it floats about seven feet above the floor of the Mediterranean's continental shelf in the beautiful blue waters off the southern coast of France. Imagine having a front door in the bottom of a building that is permanently open to the blue water below! Such is the case in this vessel. Air pressure inside keeps the water from entering the door. One diver who used this "liquid door" described the water as his blue carpet, for that is how it appeared to him from inside his underwater home.

Other buildings in the Cousteau camp serve as tool shed and garage for a two-man diving saucer. Living on the floor of the sea is becoming more and more comfortable.

The United States Navy plans a complex of dwellings on the sea floor that will consist of a combination of modular units, including a research laboratory, power sources, and living quarters. It will be built about 600 feet underwater. Such shelters will help oceanographers explore the floor and help engineers to cope with the special problems involved in undersea drilling and mining. Much more work needs to

A deep-sea submersible

Men enter a submersible before it descends into the ocean

Special seagoing crafts can carry deep-sea submersibles any place in the world

Deepstar with men aboard rises from the ocean

be done in the area of instrumentation and special tools for underwater working and living before man can make full use of this part of the earth.

One of the problems for those who have gone beneath the waters to explore the earth beneath the sea has been the problem of fresh air supply and the elimination of wastes. Recently, at the United

A helicopter lands on Jacques-Yves Cousteau's "Floating Island" laboratory

States Navy Civil Engineering Laboratory in California, a system for pulling oxygen out of seawater has been developed to supply underwater dwellings indefinitely. Some day this or a similar system may be used to supply cities on the earth under the edge of the sea. In other experiments, it has been found that test animals can be taught to breathe underwater with their own lungs. Perhaps men too may learn to do that.

Some day you may drive through

a tunnel to an underwater hotel built in the rockbed beneath the surface of the sea floor. Men are already investigating the possibility of rock sites for research and further study of earth conditions under the water. But the days of vacationing and living on the continental shelf may come long after man has learned to mine more of the materials he finds there.

Mining the Ocean

Man is already mining some re-sources from the shelf, from islands he has built in the water. At one place, sulphur is brought 2,000 feet to the surface in molten form and is transferred through steam-heated pipes to the mainland so that it stays liquid until it is ready for processing. Helicopters bring crews and supplies to the vast steel island, which is seven miles from the shore of Louisiana in the Gulf of Mexico. A sixty-room building houses the crew, and the rigs and equipment make an island that is longer than three luxury liners. From this base great quantities of sulphur are

The deep-diving saucer, Cousteau's "Denise," is actually small but capable of withstanding the great pressure of the ocean's depths

A ship docks at the world's largest offshore sulphur mine, located seven miles from land

extracted from the world's third largest deposit of sulphur, a deposit discovered in the earth beneath the edge of the sea.

Oil has long been obtained from rigs at the edge of the sea, and new knowledge provided by those who study the formations there will help provide more. Geologists believe that there is oil in quantities worth recovering under waters that are 1,000 or more feet deep. Hundreds of millions of barrels of oil are believed present in the continental shelves around the United States alone, and new methods of extracting it and transporting it to land are rapidly being developed. Recent discoveries of natural gas under the cold North Sea are bringing warmth to the homes of England, where coal and imported oil have long been the basic fuels. But they are diminishing. Much the same is true in many other parts of the earth at the edge of the sea. As nations develop and populations expand, more and more power may come from the continental shelves.

Large-scale mining of the con-

tinental shelves is being held back by lack of technique, but the future holds great promise. One exotic application of mining the ocean floor is prospecting for gold on the continental shelf off the Oregon coast under the auspices of the Oregon State University's Department of Oceanography. There, men plan to search for platinum and chromium as well.

Diamonds are the treasure being dredged from the floor of the sea near the coast of South Africa. About 700 tons of diamond gravel are wrested from the continental shelf each day with an average of five carats of diamonds per ton of earth. This compares favorably with one carat per ton from land ore, even though the underwater gravel is harder to retrieve.

The greatest mystery of the earth beneath the sea lies far beyond the continental shelf. There scientists are exploring "inner space" and making discoveries that are as exciting as those beyond the earth.

A giant offshore oil rig

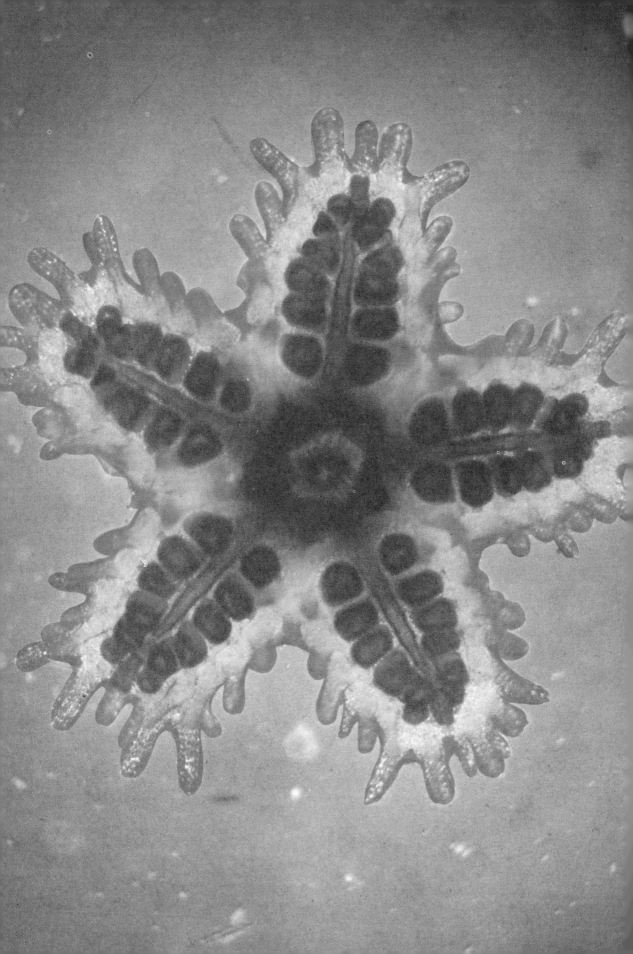

CHAPTER X

THE EARTH
BENEATH THE SEA

Most of the earth's crust lies beneath the sea, where many people picture it as a vast, flat expanse of sand. This is far from the true profile of the earth under the water.

Suppose one could look at an ocean floor from high above the earth in such a way that the water did not obscure it. One would see a spectacular array of canyons, plateaus, trenches, and other kinds of land forms. One, known as a seamount, is an "island," shaped like a mesa, whose top does not break through the ocean surface. In the fall of 1967 two unusually large seamounts were found rising from a flat plain on the bottom of the Pacific Ocean. Each is between thirty and forty miles across its summit, and one comes within 5,000 feet of the surface of the water. Although it is almost a mile below the waves, it is actually 13,800 feet high. Such a mount would be quite a sight if the waters did not cover it.

From the early days of the sea, and continuing year after year, a steady drift of debris has been raining on the ocean floor. In addition to the decaying and dead plant and animal life that falls from above, the carpet of the sea bottom has a constant supply of sediments that wash from the continents in the rivers that flow into the seas. Ocean currents sweep some of this sediment far from the coast. Desert sands are blown seaward, and they too add to the accumulation at the bottom.

At some places the sediment on the ocean floor has accumulated to a depth of 12,000 feet. Far from the coasts, oozes form the carpet, the kind depending on the variety of tiny sea animals and plants that live in the water above. In some areas, where the tiny one-celled animals called foraminifera are plentiful, the ooze is built of their shells which are made of carbonate of lime. Diatoms, microscopic plants of algae that have bizarre silicon frameworks, drop to the bottom in such quantity that they form belts of diatom ooze. One such belt stretches from Alaska to Japan under the North Pacific Ocean. Tremendous areas of the deep ocean bottom are covered with soft red clay.

Interesting scenery has long been known to exist beneath the seas, for oceanographers have been mapping ocean floors with sophisticated electronic equipment since 1945. But much remains to be discovered. For example, another recent find is an 800-mile crack in the floor of the Pacific Ocean in the area between

A starfish larva magnified forty times

the Hawaiian Islands and the Aleutians. At some places this trench is as much as fifteen miles wide.

This newly discovered crack in the ocean floor is one of a series of massive breaks that have been found in a 4,000 mile area by oceanographers who are working with the United States Environmental Services Administration (ESSA) in a project called SEAMAP. This is an intensive program aimed at mapping the bottom of the seas.

The massive breaks in the bottom of the North Pacific described above are believed to have been caused by undersea upheavals that occurred millions of years ago. There is a range of mountains over a mile and a half high near the newly discovered trough.

Men have long had charts that marked prevailing currents and some depth soundings, but today's scientists are publishing detailed maps of previously uncharted undersea mountains, mountain ridges, and sea basins for large areas. The contour of the sea bed in a 400,000-square-mile area in the North Pacific and Bering Sea has recently been made available by ESSA using information gathered from more than 275 surveys made over a two-year period. Many earthquakes are spawned each year in the area the maps cover. No wonder scientists who study the earth are especially interested in the profile of the land beneath the sea.

In spite of extensive surveys and good maps of some areas the deep ocean floor is still largely a mystery in most parts of the world. This is not surprising, because man has only recently developed equipment for its exploration and because it is such a vast area. About half the

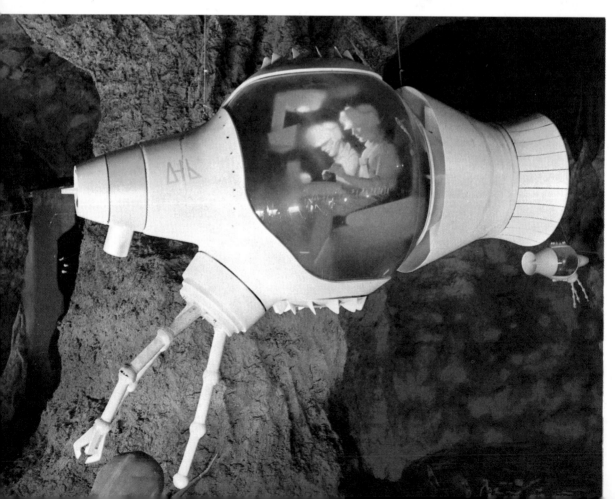

An artist's conception of a manned submersible equipped with grasping claws; the drawing has been cut away to show the interior of the craft

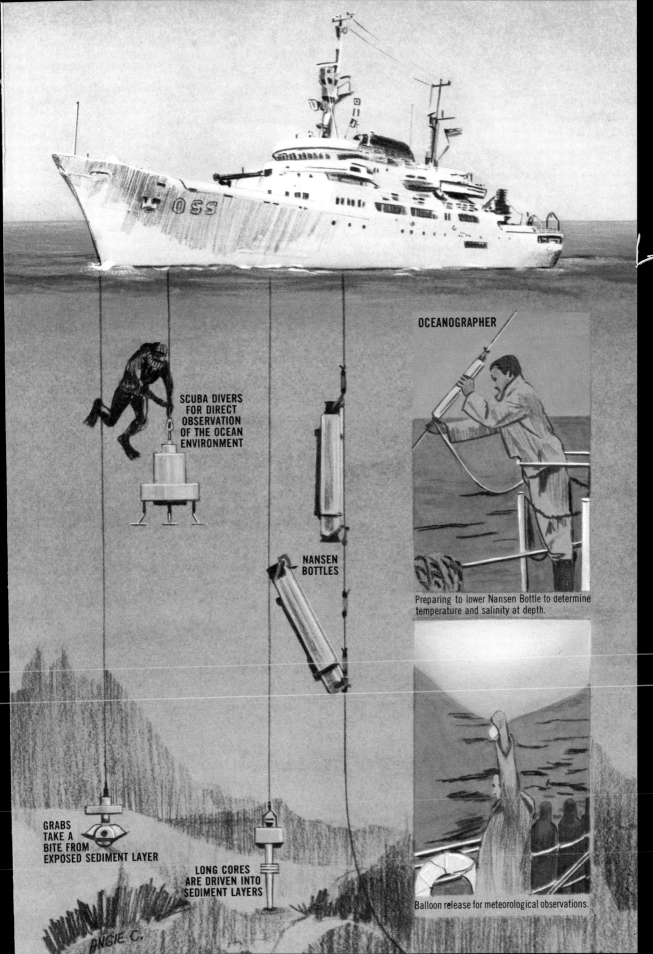

OCEANOGRAPHER

SCUBA DIVERS FOR DIRECT OBSERVATION OF THE OCEAN ENVIRONMENT

NANSEN BOTTLES

Preparing to lower Nansen Bottle to determine temperature and salinity at depth.

GRABS TAKE A BITE FROM EXPOSED SEDIMENT LAYER

LONG CORES ARE DRIVEN INTO SEDIMENT LAYERS

Balloon release for meteorological observations.

ANGIE C.

total surface of the earth is hidden under the deep waters of the oceans.

The Least Known Ocean

One of the least-known oceans has been the Indian Ocean, a body of water that covers one seventh of the planet and is the third-largest ocean in the world. Before 1958 so few research voyages had been made that scientists called it the "forlorn ocean." But in a tremendous program, known as the International Indian Ocean Expedition, twenty-three research vessels from five countries made a dent in the vast amount to be explored. One area of research was the floor, or ocean bottom, where some exciting discoveries were made.

Perhaps one of the most remarkable features of the earth's crust was discovered under the Indian Ocean. It is a wall-like ridge about 3,000 miles long and up to 13,000 feet high, running north and south in an almost straight line. It rises sharply, almost like a knife edge, from the eastern ocean basin. It has been called the 90-degree ridge, because it is located along the ninetieth meridian east of Greenwich.

Ridges, peaks, cliffs, and other formations beneath the sea would be particularly spectacular land-

Above: map of the under-sea mountain range; below: map of the undersea "crack"

During millions of years red clay accumulates in large areas of the ocean floor

scapes if they were not hidden by water. Since they are not being constantly worn away by wind, rain, and other weathering forces, underwater landscapes are sharp and jagged, much as when they had just been formed.

Abyssal plains are level areas of the sea floor, and they are some of the smoothest plains on the earth. Such level plains would form a beautiful contrast if they could be seen amidst the towering and jagged high places.

Many scientists consider the midocean ridge the most amazing feature on the earth. This enormous range of undersea mountains and valleys is probably the longest

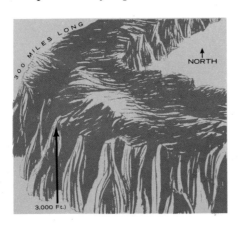

The wall-like ridge in the Indian Ocean extends for 300 miles under the water

An artist's conception of the bottom of the ocean

114

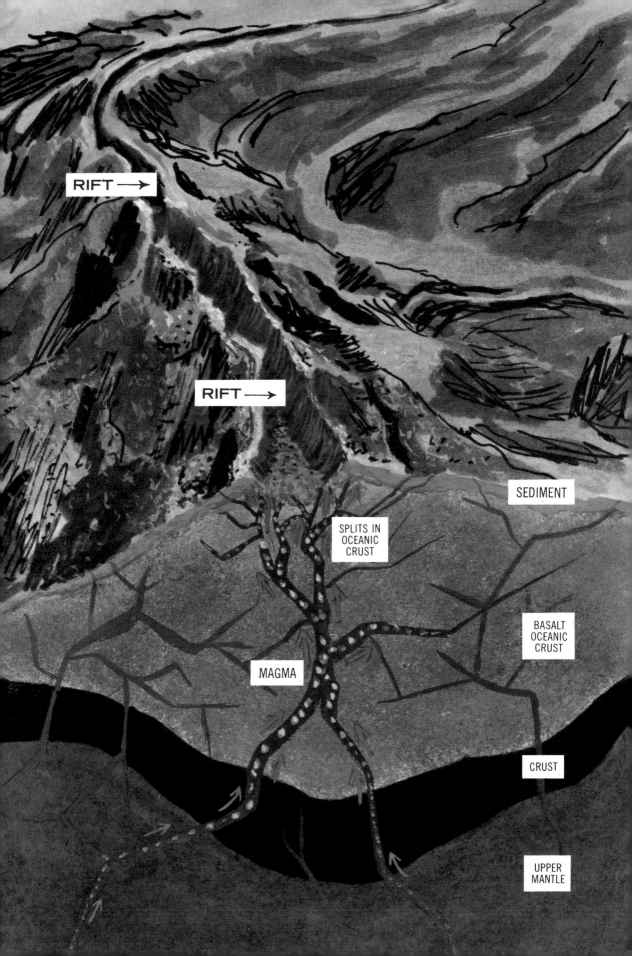

The Mid-Atlantic Ridge was probably formed by lava rising along fractures at the bottom of the sea

continuous feature in the whole world. And it may be the greatest geological discovery of modern times.

Dr. Maurice Ewing and Dr. Bruce Heezen, two very famous oceanographers from the Lamont Geological Observatory in New York, predicted such a midocean system long before the pieces were put together to show the existence of one giant mountain range about 40,000 miles long.

Oceanographers are adding another exciting feature to the system of midocean ridges with discoveries of deep rifts that cleave parts of the submarine mountain range. This midocean rift is believed to be a world-girdling fracture that generally follows the center of the midocean ridge. Although sections such as the Rift Valley in Africa are on the land part of the earth, the system lies largely underwater. Most of it has been discovered within recent years, although scientists had laid out a pattern where they believed such a rift might be before the pieces of the path were put together. They did this by plotting data collected from records of ocean-bottom earthquakes on a world-wide scale.

What caused such amazing and tremendous features as this ridge and rift in the earth's crust? That is another question that puzzles geologists. There are several theories. For example, many scientists believe that hot rock in the deep earth may be creeping upward. After forming the ridge, it split the crust of the earth and formed the rift down the center. Such movements continue, accounting for new clefts, volcanoes, and earthquakes in these regions.

Another theory is that the lighter part of the hot rock deep in the earth separates from the rest and rises to the surface, forming ridges.

No matter what the cause, there is dramatic evidence that molten rock flowed from the midocean ridge and spread out on both sides of it, as mentioned earlier. Although a movement of two to three inches per year is very small when compared with the size of the ocean

Undersea upheavals cause massive breaks in undersea rocks

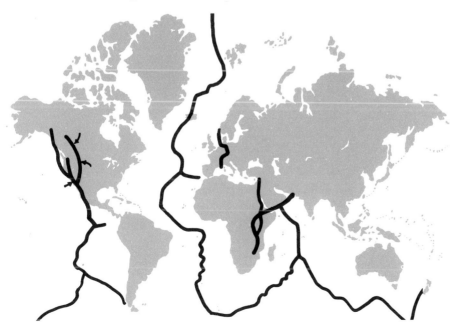

Huge cracks extend for thousands of miles over the surface of the world; most of them are under the ocean

floor, it is a strange action. And as the sea floor spreads, the continents may be moving, too. This quiet action of the earth is another of its mysteries.

The ocean bottom is little known today in spite of the work of oceanographers around the world. Men from many countries work side by side in this exciting exploration, which is leading to a better understanding of the earth's crust. In the

A research submarine, the Aluminaut, scouts the bottom of the ocean

case of the Indian Ocean bottom ridge described on page 114, the data were compiled by George Peter, a native of Budapest, Hungary, and by Omar DeWald, a native of Williamsport, Pennsylvania.

Analysis of data requires months of intensive study in spite of the use of highly sophisticated electronic equipment. Even with computers and electronic equipment that utilizes sound waves to determine the

In Florida a skin diver inspects a coral growth

The remarkable research ship FLIP can be partly submerged so that scientists are able to study conditions below the sea's surface

ocean's depths, the height of mountains, the topography of the sea bed, and what lies beneath it, mapping the ocean floor is a gigantic task that will go on for many years.

A program to test a theory may require a global effort and tremendous amounts of money, men, and equipment, and it may require a considerable amount of time. Such is the case in the program to test theories such as the one that soft rock is being pushed out constantly from the midocean ridges. Preparations were underway in the fall of 1967 for the project known as JOIDES (Joint Oceanographic Institutions for Deep Earth Sampling). Under the direction of the University of California's Scripps Institu-

The research ship FLIP in position; the bow of the ship is several feet underwater

Coming up again

tion of Oceanography and with the cooperation of the University of Miami's Institute of Marine Sciences, Woods Hole Oceanographic Institution at Woods Hole, Massachusetts, and the Lamont Geological Observatory of Columbia University, a whole year was set aside for planning alone. Scientists from other organizations are joining the project, and the whole world is the laboratory.

American oceanographers in the Project JOIDES plan to drill a series of holes in the ocean floor in hopes of solving a number of problems. One is the controversial continental drift theory discussed earlier in this book. Large numbers of cores from the sea floor could provide more evidence about magnetic patterns that show the striped arrangement on either side of the midocean ridges. From holes drilled in the bottom of the sea may come further information about the evolution of the earth, its age, climates and currents that existed millions of years ago, and the origin of various features of the underwater landscape. It is a big adventure that may help solve many of the riddles of the ocean floor.

Long lists of modern instruments help today's explorers of the floor of the sea. For example, the drillers of project JOIDES will benefit from experience gained in the Mohole Project. But none of the seventy sites that have been selected for core drilling will involve such deep drilling, as that planned for "Moho." Drills will be sent through four miles of water to penetrate about 2,000 feet of sediment and crust of the earth, so chances of success are far greater.

New Research Ships

New research ships help those who search beneath today's oceans. For instance, the research vessel FLIP can lift itself upright to become a stationary laboratory on any of the seven seas. FLIP is a floating instrument platform that is usable in water at any depth. It belongs to the University of California's Scripps Institution of Oceanography and is towed by another craft to wherever scientists want to work.

Suppose men want to shift the FLIP from horizontal to vertical position after it has been towed to the work area. A series of ballast tanks are filled with water in the hull of the ship, and the weight gradually sinks the stern. When it is time to reverse the position, compressed air is used to blow the water from the ballast tanks, and the ship returns to its horizontal position.

The science of oceanics is young indeed, and man is just beginning to learn about the hidden floor. But the potential for future use may be great.

CHAPTER XI

THE EARTH
IS MAN'S
SPACE SHIP

The solid earth beneath your feet is no longer considered such a firm one. Today, geologists and those who follow some of their explorations realize why the geology exhibit at EXPO 67, Canada's World's Fair, was identified by a pot of bubbling tomato soup. The froth on the soup was likened to continents of the earth, while the clear broth that caused the froth by its churning was likened to the activity in the viscous layer which may begin about 30 miles below the surface of the earth and reach a depth of about 300 miles. The model was Professor Tuzo Wilson's way of calling attention to the dynamic nature of man's home planet. The earth is being recognized, at last, as a place of tremendous action both in local areas and, on a far greater scale, beneath its crust.

Why do men care about the earth's crust and the part deep inside? Why do they spend millions of dollars in research? Why do thousands of men devote their lives to learning more about the planet on which men have lived for so long without much knowledge of it?

For scientists, the reason for studying the earth may well be the earth itself. Its amazing features, its riddles, its wonders are enough. They investigate science for science's sake. The rest of the people who live on the planet owe such men a great debt.

As the population explodes, knowledge of the earth in action becomes more and more important. Experts have long been predicting an unbearably crowded earth for the future, an earth in which every bit of living space will be filled and the supply of food, fuel, and other resources will be more limited.

With the prospects of "standing room only" on a planet that is already overcrowded in many places, the study of the earth itself grows in importance day by day. Much as the crew riding in a space ship depend on a life-support system to fulfill their needs, all men on the earth are riding a giant space ship, and their trip depends on how they handle the support system beneath their feet.

Man cannot stretch the earth, but the more he understands about its structure, its crust, and its movements, the more he can use it to his advantage.

Minerals from the Sea

Many people think that the real promise of the future lies in the earth beneath the seas. The mining of minerals from the deep ocean

MANGANESE

NICKEL

COPPER

Various minerals can be found along the floor of the ocean

In the future men may build cities under the sea

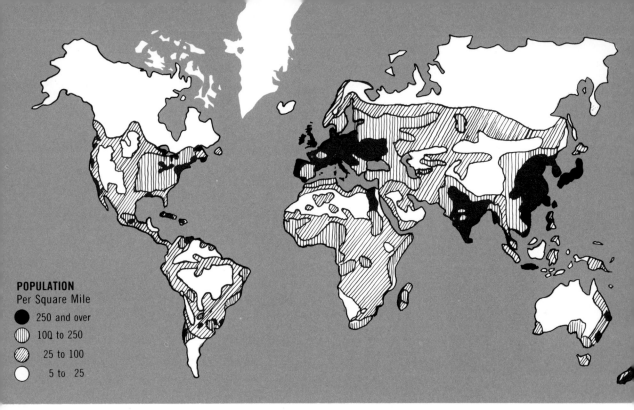

POPULATION
Per Square Mile

- 250 and over
- 100 to 250
- 25 to 100
- 5 to 25

Man lives in those places of the world where the food supply is most plentiful

might someday, they hope, mean the end of world poverty and help on the road to peace. Certainly, minerals have been found in many areas. There are, for example, recent discoveries of manganese nodules on the floor of the Indian Ocean, as well as on those of the Pacific and the Atlantic, and perhaps there are many more that have not been discovered.

Manganese is scarce in the United States, so this is one of the cases in which men are already comparing the cost of extracting it from the sea with the cost of importing it or refining low-grade ores available in the land. Dr. John Mero, vice president of Ocean Resources, Inc., believes that it may already be profitable to mine phosphate, nickel, copper, and cobalt as well as manganese from the sea at today's costs.

With materials becoming more scarce, men are becoming more conscious of pollution. To what extent is man contaminating the treasures of the earth that he may

need in the future?

The oceans have long been a great trash can. Many geologists are questioning the effect on living things in the ocean of the discharge of radioactive materials into the sea, and on the bottom of the sea.

In November, 1967, Dr. Arvid Pardo urged the negotiation of a treaty through the United Nations to ensure peaceful developments of the sea bottom's resources for the benefit of all mankind. He estimated that by the decade 1980 to 1990 commercial farming of kelp, a seaweed, and fish farming would be practical from underwater quarters where "farmers" could store equipment and live for weeks at a time.

Resources Tomorrow

The men of tomorrow may make better use of the resources of the land part of the earth, too. Certainly they can make use of many technological improvements and stretch the supplies of ores that can be extracted from the ground. For example, today's scientists are experimenting with the use of nuclear explosions to release natural gas and oil that is locked beneath the surface of the earth. In the United States some groups are also investigating the possibility of blasting copper ores from hidden sites in the earth through underground nuclear explosions. Someday men may be able to process tens of millions of tons of copper ore that today is unreachable.

In contrast to the latest methods of increasing man's benefits from the earth in both mining and food production are some of the ways in which the people of less wealthy nations are increasing their limited supply on resources. Although the rhythmic rise and fall of the tides sometimes creates a limited amount of new land by building up sandbars, land at the edge of the water in other areas is being washed into

Men, women, and children carry baskets of soil to build a sea wall to reclaim needed land.

the sea. In Pakistan, soil in the fertile Ganges Delta is being lost for still another reason. Seawater intrudes on the soil and reduces the amount of food that can be produced.

Imagine men, women, and children filling baskets of soil and carrying them on their heads to help build an earth wall to prevent seawater from spoiling their farmland and to reclaim some that has already been made salty. A chain of dikes about 2,600 miles long is being built by manual labor, for bulldozers and heavy earth-moving equipment are not available. Using a small loan from the United States Agency for International Development, as many as 150,000 people may be working at one time in each of twelve sectors to block the sea with dikes. Some of the banks must be as high as twenty-four feet. But when the work is completed, about 2.7 million additional acres of arable land will help feed four million people in that area.

Today's scientists look to reclamation, to better mining methods, to advances in agriculture, to new ways of using the sea, and to many other approaches to the problem of meeting the needs of the growing population that is crowding the earth.

Someday, parts of the earth in the deserts, both hot and cold, may be made fertile and comfortable enough for people in large numbers.

Certainly, man is just beginning to understand the great forces which are at work deep in the earth. By learning more about the earth's history and the actions that are taking place in the earth from the seemingly quiet part beneath our feet to the depths, geologists are helping those who ride the space ship Planet Earth.

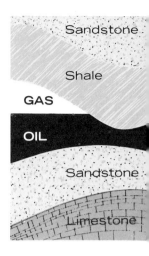

Atomic explosions might be used to release gas and oil

125

Asimov, Isaac, *To the Ends of the Universe.* Walker & Company, 1967.
Cloos, Hans, *Conversation with the Earth.* Knopf, 1953.
Dyson, James, *World of Ice.* Knopf, 1962.
Engel, Leonard, *Sea.* Time-Life, 1967.
Gamow, George, *Planet Called Earth.* Viking, 1963.
Hall, Jennie, *Buried Cities.* Macmillan, 1964.
Irving, Robert, *Volcanoes and Earthquakes.* Knopf, 1962.
Lobeck, Armin K., *Things Maps Don't Tell Us.* Macmillan, 1956.
Pearl, Richard M., *1001 Questions Answered About the Mineral Kingdom.* Dodd, Mead, 1959.
Pough, Frederick H., *All About Volcanoes and Earthquakes.* Random House, 1953.
Pough, Frederick H., *Field Guide to Rocks and Minerals.* Houghton Mifflin, 1953.
Reed, W. Maxwell, *Earth for Sam.* Harcourt, Brace & World, 1960.
Smith, Howard E., Jr., *From Under the Earth: America's Metals, Fuels and Minerals.* Harcourt, Brace & World, 1967.
Stephans, William M., *Science Beneath the Sea: The Story of Oceanography.* Putnam, 1966.
Sutton, Ann and Myron, *Life of the Desert.* McGraw-Hill, 1966.
Wycoff, Jerome, *Geology.* Golden Press, 1967.
Zim, Herbert, and Paul Shaefer, *Rocks and Minerals.* Golden Press, 1957.

Picture Credits

Cover: Werner Stoy from Freelance Photographers Guild

Illustrations, maps and charts by Angeline V. Culfogienis

Photographs: *6:* Photograph from the Mount Wilson and Palomar Observatories *9–10:* NASA *12–13:* NASA *15:* Photographs from the Mount Wilson and Palomar Observatories *16:* ESSA Photo *23:* United Press International Photo; Courtesy of the American Museum of Natural History *24:* A.E.C. *25:* The Bergman Associates; Courtesy of the American Museum of Natural History *26:* The Bergman Associates; Courtesy of the American Museum of Natural History *28:* I. J. Witkind for the U.S. Geological Survey *32–33:* The Bergman Associates *34:* Courtesy of the American Museum of Natural History; Swiss National Tourist Office *35:* N. W. Ayer & Son, Inc. *36:* United States Department of Agriculture *36–37:* Werner Stoy from Freelance Photographers Guild; Standard Oil Company *37:* USDA-Soil Conservation Service *38:* Photo Courtesy Pan American Airways *39:* Dennis Hallinan from Freelance Photographers Guild; USDA-Soil Conservation Service *44:* U.S. Navy Official Photo *44–45:* Freelance Photographers Guild *46–47–48:* ESSA Photos *50:* Wide World Photos *51–52:* ESSA Photos *55–56:* ESSA Photos *57:* Lehigh University *58:* Chrisman from Freelance Photographers Guild *59:* The Bergman Associates *60:* Villiger Gstaad from Freelance Photographers Guild; U.S. Navy Official Photo *62:* U.S. Navy Official Photo *65–66:* U.S. Navy Official Photo *67:* ESSA Photo *68–69–70:* Standard Oil Company *72:* Marie Shaw *74:* Marie Shaw; Swiss National Tourist Office *76:* The Bergman Associates *79:* Courtesy of the American Museum of Natural History; The Bergman Associates; Mobil Oil Corporation *80:* ESSA Photo *81:* NASA *82:* Werner Stoy from Freelance Photographers Guild *84:* Wide World Photo *85–86:* United Press International Photos *88:* Wide World Photos *89:* Culver Pictures, Inc. *90–91–92:* Werner Stoy from Freelance Photographers Guild *93:* James K. Davis *94:* U.S. Navy Official Photo *98–99:* U.S. Coast Guard Official Photo *99–100:* U.S. Navy Official Photo *102–103–104:* Westinghouse Photo *104–105:* Lockheed Missiles & Space Company *105:* Westinghouse Photo *106–107:* French Embassy Press & Information Division *108:* Freelance Photographers Guild *109:* Standard Oil Company *110:* The Bergman Associates *112:* General Motors Corporation *117:* Anne Marie Jauss (Map) *118:* Reynolds Metals Company *119:* Florida Development Commission *120–121:* Photos courtesy of U.S. Steel/Scripps Institution of Oceanography, University of California, San Diego *122:* General Motors Corporation.

Photo Researcher: Shirley Zimmerman